BORROWING
the EYES *of others*

By the same author

BORROWING
the EYES *of others*

Reflecting with Paintings
Volume 1

DENIS MCBRIDE

A Redemptorist Publication

Copyright © Denis McBride, 2008

Published by **Redemptorist Publications**
A Registered Charity limited by guarantee. Registered in England 3261721.

First published June 2008

Layout and cover design by Rosemarie Pink

Front cover illustration used by kind permission of Fernando Botero

ISBN 978-0-85231-351-0

A CIP catalogue record for this book is available from the British Library

Printed by Estudios Graficos Zure, Spain

Redemptorist
PUBLICATIONS

Alphonsus House Chawton Hampshire GU34 3HQ
Telephone 01420 88222   01420 88805
rp@rpbooks.co.uk   www.rpbooks.co.uk

Preface

Dear Reader,

This is not a book of poetry but of prose reflections, which are spread out lazily and extravagantly as real poetry is on the page. This arrangement is to slow you down, hopefully aiding reflection.

When I wrote the book *The Parables of Jesus,* I was intrigued at how Jesus did so much of his teaching through the medium of fiction, using imaginative language to communicate some signature of the beauty of the kingdom of God. Whereas Jesus never states what the kingdom of God actually is, he seems happy to capture *something* of its truth through the parables: "The kingdom of God is like…"

The parables of Jesus emerged from an oral culture, where almost every form of education and enlightenment came by hearing. The great loss in oral culture was, of course, forgetting what you had heard, so, as Walter Ong points out in his study of orality and literacy, it was important to communicate memorable thoughts that could be recalled easily.* Vivid, pictorial language – rather than abstract thought – became the standard vehicle of communication because that kind of language is easy to remember and the best way of aiding understanding.

Paintings, too, have their own language, from representative, to coded, to abstract, to you-name-it – communicating another world to the onlooker, another slant on looking at people and things, another way of appreciating colour and texture and form, or simply to provoke unspoken communication between the artist's emotions and the viewer's.

These reflections were originally written for a retreat, "Reflecting on Paintings". The reflections are, I think, better heard than read. I offered the reflections in an attempt to invite people to look at selected paintings, to imagine another world, and then to return to their own story in the hope that some inner conversation might be provoked through the strange encounters.

Just as in the Gospels, not all the characters that appear in the following pages are upright or impeccable; since all communities are a mixture of the good and the bad, the wise and the foolish, the crooked and the cracked, I have

---

* W. Ong, *Orality and Literacy* (New York: Methuen, 1982), 16-30.

reflected that variance in the voices. The contrast and conflict in the Gospel narratives are not only between characters, but – more importantly – within characters. The Gospel patchwork of contrasting characters and outlooks is repeated in the world of the parables – where we see how "the good and the bad alike" are sought out and invited to table (Matthew 22:10), and we are asked to learn from such shady characters as the dishonest steward, a desperado who ensures his future by lucrative arithmetic (Luke 16:1-10).

Within single Gospel characters you can detect commitment and fickleness, virtue and contempt, kindness and stupidity. You watch a tender-hearted but foolish father divide his property only to discover that he has effectively split up his family; you watch a dutiful king organise a splendid feast for his son's wedding and you're surprised when he ends up torching a town to cinders; you hear a virtuous man pray in the Temple only to witness his prayer being rejected because of his well-nursed snobbery. We learn from teachers steeped in muddle and contradiction.

There is a clear sense in the Gospels that you can learn from anyone – not only in the parables, but in the main narrative. You are invited to learn from a little child, from a woman who is an accomplished sinner, from a vacillating governor, even from a disciple who denies his Lord to a little girl who opens night-doors. It is not only those who are wise and enlightened, the teachers and the prophets, who can help us to learn. Anyone can be our teacher: "Truly I tell you, wherever the Gospel is proclaimed throughout the world, this story will be proclaimed in memory of her" (Mark 14:9).

It is in this understanding that I offer these voices, which speak through the paintings. While the paintings have their own distinctive authority and need no commentary, I have used them as a mirror to reflect on a variety of issues. I hope you enjoy the text as well as you will surely enjoy the paintings; I hope, too, that at least some of the voices speak to your heart.

Sincerely,

Denis McBride
Alphonsus House
Chawton
Hampshire
England

Contents

Old Woman Praying the Rosary
Paul Cézanne

Praying the rosary

For Mary and Danny Ferry

I'm just finishing the fourth decade
of the Joyful Mysteries of the rosary,
the Presentation of Jesus in the Temple.
I'm up here, alone in the attic room
of my daughter's rather grand house –
I believe estate agents call it a Victorian villa –
in Bayswater, in London,
far away from my home place
in the lonely hills and wet bogland of Donegal.
No villas where I come from, believe me.

My clever daughter, Mary Frances,
a computer graphics designer
with a salary that looks like a telephone number,
said that this room would be reserved for me –
"Granny's room" is what the four boys always call it
even when I'm not here, which I think is nice –
and she had the room decorated specially for me.
"It'll be a sympathetic reflection, Mammy," she said,
"of your own style and colouring."
I never knew I had either,
and I could swear she called it "the distressed look".

Sacred Heart of Jesus, look kindly on me,
for I know I'm no Christmas-card Madonna,
but if I looked like the walls of this room,
wouldn't I have been already handed over
to the undertaker, to make something of me?

I come from heather, rock, wind, rain,
loch, bog, mountain, sea:

my roots are landscape looking out
to the vast brooding deep of the Atlantic Ocean.
When I sit in the porch at home and look out,
the next stop on the map is Boston.
Many did leave and head in that direction
to seek their fortune, God bless their need.

A few miles to the back of me is Muckish Mountain,
the most northerly summit of the Derryveagh Mountains.
A hulking landmark, its shape is what many emigrants
from these parts took with them as a memento of home
as they left for Scotland or England,
the United States or Australia.
Emigrants who came from the west of Muckish,
from the majestic spread and stillness of Gweedore,
heading first for Letterkenny,
then for the leaving harbour of Derry,
would first cross what the locals called the Bridge of Tears.

Their families and friends – followed by a scatter of dogs –
would accompany them as far as the bridge
and there they would hold each other blindly,
pressing their farewells, bruising one another's flesh,
hoping to make up for so much left unsaid.
The ones who were left behind would sigh and wave
and watch as their loved ones gradually diminished
and then disappeared – some for ever –
through Muckish Gap.
Then the assembled gathering would turn away,
one by one, each feeling forlorn and somehow stranded.
One by one, each would turn away
from the sight of Muckish Gap
to a larger gap; return to what was left of home.

Who leaves now from the Bridge of Tears?

Now emigration from Ireland has been reduced to a trickle
and so many emigrants seem to be returning.
Some have come back to build houses,
assert their claim in breeze blocks,
then head back to their real lives elsewhere.

Why does no one repair the old
and remake the home-place?
The old places are pulled down or left untended
while everyone builds from scratch
as if the past can no longer be supported,
is somehow unfit for reinforcement.
These days the exiles are coming back in droves
and building yellow-painted houses
at the end of their yellow-brick roads:
loneliness come home to roost.

I leave Ireland for only two weeks in the summer
to come here for a holiday
(Mary Frances pays the ticket: Ryan Air)
and the time is arranged when the family returns
from their other villa, overlooking Lake Nemi
in the Alban Hills –
aren't they near neighbours to the Pope
who's just up the road at Castel Gandolfo!
Anyway, when I come over for my holiday
my daughter arranges for the family
to get together on a Friday after supper
to pray the rosary. Strange this,
since Mary Frances has lost her faith.

She does it, she says, to remind her of her childhood –
all of us there,
way back then,
huddled together in the big kitchen,
with our backs to one another,

hardening our knees on the flagstones,
with the turf fire roaring away,
and the repetitive murmur of Hail Marys
filling the night air;
most people count the Hail Marys on their fingers,
forgetting the beads,
with everyone checking the arithmetic of ten
between the Our Father and the Glory be.

Sometimes the telling of the beads
would be sprinkled with suppressed giggles
when old Uncle Din would give out
one of his ferocious farts!
God have mercy on the old soul,
but I remember well that his humming interruptions
became an expected part of the round:
the rosary was never the same
without one of Uncle Din's peculiar ejaculations,
and wouldn't he, in all fairness to the man,
usually manage to hold it in
until a Glory be to the Father?

I know that Mary Frances,
God look down on her and the family,
doesn't have the family rosary
on Fridays when I'm not here;
she does it to please me, I know;
it does, I suppose, gladden me in a way.
She wants to introduce the four boys
to this "sacred memory" of hers,
but it feels a bit like an old performance,
a re-enaction of some daft ancient ritual.
Sometimes, in the middle of the recital,
I feel we're like lost souls
waiting for a real plot to get us going.

I mean, when you love something like the rosary,
you don't want it to be "treasured"
as if it were some antique heirloom
handed down through generations
and kept in the display cabinet;
you want to hug it to yourself tight, like I do,
use it as the life-line it is,
a prayerful binding to the God of all consolation
who looks down on us all.

Mary Frances is in love with a past
she now holds in custody.
She loves quoting the poet Seamus Heaney:

> Polished linoleum shone there. Brass taps shone.
> The china cups were very white and big –
> An unchipped set with sugar bowl and jug.
> The kettle whistled. Sandwich and teascone
> Were present and correct. In case it run,
> The butter must be kept out of the sun.
> And don't be dropping crumbs. Don't tilt your chair.
> Don't reach. Don't point. Don't make noise when you stir.

For her, the rosary belongs in that setting
of linoleum and whistling kettles and childhood injunctions,
a tableau from a simpler past,
to be preserved but not refreshed.
I have no idea what she worships now.

Personally, dear onlooker, I've always believed
in having something grander than an old queen
to genuflect before, however nice she is,
something larger than the man-size world
we all inhabit, to bow before.
If there is a God –
and even at my age I would have a wee "if" there,

for isn't one of my sons a grand theologian
lecturing in Maynooth on the existence of God,
though he has reservations about angels –
but if there is a God, shouldn't we recognise
a larger and kindlier presence than ourselves;
acknowledge that we are not the summit of everything?

Sure, isn't that what prayer is?

The family rosary here in Bayswater is,
I have to say, a bit of a jumble,
with the four boys racing over the beads,
rushing headlong through the Hail Marys
and making a beeline for the big Amen at the end.
I know, God keep them from all harm,
that they're not thinking of the mysteries
but roaming somewhere else in their heads –
probably rehearsing a new role on PlayStation;
but for all that, the four of them are good wee souls
and would never harm man or beast.

I know the boys go to church only when I'm here,
and all four traipse along with me, kindly,
to the sung noon Mass at St Mary of the Angels
and endure what can only be mystical boredom to them:
I always console myself that they haven't left the Church
because they never belonged to it in the first place,
so there's no point in blaming them for anything.
(I'm not a hard woman, dear onlooker,
in spite of the fact that our postmistress once said
I had the predatory snout of a hawk!
Imagine the gall of the woman!)

No, the boys are good and decent, but I cannot help feeling
they belong to a lost generation
who belong only to themselves.

I do worry: it must be very lonely sometimes,
having nothing to fall back on but yourself,
confined within the limits of your own little world.
Where do you go
when your whole world collapses?
Don't you think we need a larger story than ourselves
to connect to, when the sun and the moon
and all the stars gradually dim into blackout
and you feel hopelessly alone?
I wish the boys had something larger on their horizon
than trivial victories on "virtual reality".

Why, dear onlooker, can't we keep the people we want?
Why do our beliefs, handed over with care
and drilled into our own children,
fade so quickly in a generation?
Why does what we treasure end up so quickly
on the skip outside our children's new houses?
God look down on the boys kindly,
but they seem to have caught nothing of the faith
from their mother, who once believed so keenly.
God love them dearly;
sure don't I love them to bits myself?

And their father?
Isn't he the most gorgeous man
that ever stepped on a Persian carpet?
Mohamed Ahmad is a Muslim, from Iran,
though I think he said his mother
was a Shona from Zimbabwe.
Anyway, he could kill you with his good looks.
And doesn't he just love me
in the old bonnet covering my hair
and the long skirt down to my ankles,
like I'm one of his own,
a walking promotion for sharia law?

Didn't he once say that he'd love
Mary Frances to dress like me?
(He'd say that only once to our Mary Frances.)

When he gave a speech on my eightieth birthday,
one he crafted with great care,
he toasted what he called
"the modesty of your bearing, dear Mama Mary,
and your earth-hardened hands,
those scoops that have quarried hard ground
and coaxed five children into adulthood".
(He reads a lot of poetry, I think.)
God look down on him tenderly,
but I have never met a nicer man
who cherishes me with such affection.

Where I come from,
most men are naturally a bit chary about the women –
maybe rooted in the old Catholic pause about difference?
Don't we have more bachelors in Ireland per square mile
than they have sheep in Australia?
Anyway, Mohamed Ahmad has his own little beads
which he fingers every day, without fail,
even, I know, when I'm not here.
I've seen him pray five times a day –
a bit like my five decades –
no matter who's there or who's looking,
kneeling down on his wee rug, inclining forward
and murmuring away to himself, "Allahu Akbar."
Don't I love to see him praying away to Allah!

To be frank with you, sometimes I wonder
if I have more in common with him
than with my own crowd…

I know the boys sometimes go with him
to the Regent's Park Mosque on a Friday,
but the mosque, they tell me,
is as puzzling to them as the Mass.
Little Jojo, the youngest child
and an absolute dote if ever I laid eyes on one,
loves the rosary beads,
and wears them round his neck at weekends
ever since he saw a picture of David Beckham,
on Google images, he said,
wearing them in Japan.
May the good Lord look kindly on us all,
but I have no idea what football or Google
or Japan has to do with rosary beads,
but who am I to be talking?

Every day I say the rosary on my own,
before I climb into bed,
kneeling down before a crucifix.
Mary Frances bought a beautiful figure
of the crucified Jesus, without the cross,
on a rainy Saturday on the Portobello Road
and put it on my wall here
("an antique Flemish corpus" she called it)
and I'm kneeling before it now –
sadly, dear onlooker, it's just out of your view –
though I hear that crucifixes
might soon be out of everyone's view.

Isn't there an article in the paper today
reporting that crucifixes are being thrown out
of schools and colleges
because they are seen as fanatic images,
offensive signs to those of other beliefs and none?
God protect us from the eejits that govern over us,
but we'll soon be outlawing belief in God,

considering it to be unmannerly, even outrageous,
vexing to the old floozies who run county councils,
who hector everyone on political correctness,
and want nothing as strong as personal faith
to interfere with their "non-discriminatory policies".
Who on God's earth thinks up this gobbledygook?
They might as well organise oblivion –
everyone is the same in the dark –
settle into the misery of the average,
and call it the new age.

And to think of himself on the cross,
didn't he die for all of us?
"For you and for all," as it says in Holy Mass.
God be between us and all harm
but I don't know what the world is coming to,
I really don't.

I'd better get back to the rosary,
otherwise I'll be scraping the floor all night with my knees,
and the right one is wonderfully wobbly.
The rosary keeps me calm,
just like the ironing,
and I find telling the beads a soft close to the day,
whispering away to God
in the rhythm of the repeated prayers.

I'm now into the fifth and final decade,
the Finding of Jesus in the Temple.
This one has always flummoxed me, you know:
how could Jesus, at twelve years old,
just sneak off all on his own
without telling his parents where he was heading?
What kind of example is that to set for young ones?
It took Mary and Joseph three days before
they eventually found the little upstart in the Temple.

I suppose if little Jojo –
he's around the same age –
ran off on me one day up the town,
the last place I'd look for him would be in the cathedral,
more likely the HMV store, in the games section.

In the Temple you see this adult child being clever
with all the gobsmacked professors taking notes –
nothing backward or shy about him –
while no one has a mind to see
the hurt coming through the door.
When Mary points out
how worried she and Joseph have been,
all she gets in return is the cocky reply,
"I must be about my Father's business" –
so boo to the two of you, can't you see I'm busy?

Well, I tell you, if one of my own talked to me like that,
no matter if he'd come from the bosom of God,
never mind the bosom of Abraham,
I'd give him a skite around the ear, I would,
and tell him to get himself up the road, sharpish.

Over the years I've collected books of Old Master paintings
on the Madonna and Child – I love the theme –
with the child Jesus cleaving to his mother, Mary,
sometimes clutching her breast,
hanging on for dear life,
hungry for his mother's tender look.
But the Finding of Jesus in the Temple
is poles apart from all this:
there is no softness, no hands entwining,
no leaning into one another,
no speechless gaze of love;
now is a world away from then,
and now there are only hard words exchanged,

self-reliance and separation,
or as dear Jojo might say,
"attitude with no pity".

Then, if I remember the story right,
it says somewhere after this,
"Mary stored up all these things in her heart."
This is a line that goes through me
because of the wild hurt it hides
behind the spare phrasing.
Sometimes language conceals
more than it gives away, distracting us
from the sorrowful things at the heart of the joyful.
I think this decade, to be honest,
should be in the Sorrowful Mysteries.

The poor soul, what Our Lady has to endure!
Mary, like all mothers, has to keep
a whole bunch of worries tucked away
out of sight and earshot of others –
unease about what the family is up to,
apprehension about what will become of them,
worrying about whether she is doing the right thing
or trying to unearth what it was she did wrong –
stuff she doesn't dare share with anyone.
She gathers them all to herself
and how soon they all crowd in
until the heart looks like an emergency ward
in a blackout in the blitz
and she is at the end of her tether.

Just like all mothers do,
everywhere around the world,
whatever race or colour or creed;
just like I do with my own crowd,
every day that goes by

and every night that falls
from the courtesy of the good Lord.

That is why I am here, on my knees,
in my very own "distressed" attic,
praying the rosary.

I'd better finish now and say the final prayer,
and maybe, dear onlooker, you would join me?

> *O God, whose only begotten Son,*
> *by his life, death, and resurrection,*
> *has purchased for us the rewards of eternal salvation,*
> *grant, we beseech thee,*
> *that, meditating on these mysteries*
> *of the most holy Rosary of the Blessed Virgin Mary,*
> *we may both imitate what they contain*
> *and obtain what they promise,*
> *through Christ our Lord.*
> *Amen.*

Goodnight now,
and may God in his kindness
keep you from all harm.

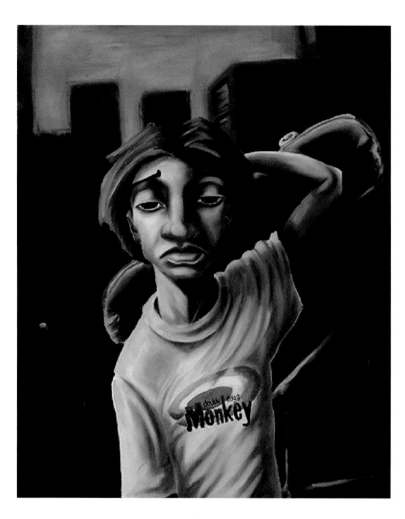

Jojo
JW Miller

Growing up hyphenated

For the Catholic School Principals of
Western Australia

Hi, guys, my name is Jonathan Joseph –
people call me Jojo.
You probably met my Gran earlier
saying her rosary up in the attic;
it's her bedtime chatroom with God,
and she could have her own blog on the internet,
updated after every decade when she rests a little.
I've listened in many times to what she says
and she chats away – the diary of a sumptuous mind –
alerting God to what is unravelling now.

I know she's chatted to you
but I bet she didn't tell you
what only I know in the family:
that after she's prayed the rosary,
she lifts the corner of the mattress
and, like a bomb-disposal expert
carefully extracting the firing pin,
she removes her old clay pipe!
She unwraps the cloth that holds the pipe,
and there's a block of Warhorse tobacco,
a little penknife and a box of matches.

She slices off a few thin cuts from the block,
rubs them between her two palms, to soften them,
then fingers her delicious into the pipe.
Moving over to the fireplace,
with her back to the crucifix,
she "hunkers down" as she calls it on her knees,

lights up and puffs away in holy contentment
while directing the smoke, ever so carefully,
to disappear up the chimney!
I know coz she always calls me in to guard the door
in case of a surprise visitor;
but there never is.

Wicked she is!
Everyone should have a Gran like her;
really does her own thing, independent like,
dressing according to her own tastes
rather than being a fashion groupie –
none of those Oscar-award outfits for her
with bling to weigh her down.
I really admire her coz she doesn't care,
apart from the secret smoke, what people think about her.
"Just my rum little ways, Jojo," she always says.

My friends are crazy about her
coz she's got such street cred.
When we go out with her we all get such a buzz –
I mean it's like going out with a prize exhibit
from Madame Tussaud's Waxworks Museum,
like having your own piece of art with you!
Sol, my best friend, who is Jamaican-Portuguese-English,
said it all when he said:
"Your Gran is no eye-candy, dog,
but she's fresh, a real playa."
He reckoned Gran could launch a new street style:
Irish Gothic or Pensioner Punk.

One day we left Gran standing outside
the Virgin Megastore in Piccadilly Circus,
and when we came out she was shaking with laughter
coz some people had given her money

thinking she was a homeless bag-lady
or had run out of copies of the *Big Issue.*
She gave all the coins to me –
thirteen pounds and seven pence –
her favourite charity, she said.

Though she looks a bit severe in the painting you saw,
she's great fun, or "the best of crack" as she would say,
and she's always joking about her age and ailments.
"Old age", she says, "is when you sink your teeth
into a juicy steak and they stay there!"
And she's really mean on PlayStation:
those old fingers don't just travel the beads
but down Apache helicopters before you can say Glory be.

When people see Gran and me walking down the street,
they can't work out the relationship between us.
We must look like extras from two different films,
Gran from *The Quiet Man*
and me, a Hobbit, from *Lord of the Rings.*
I know I look a bit strange – Dad's African-Iranian
and Mum's Irish, after all –
so I don't know how many hyphens I have.
"Mixed race" they call it these days
and I guess I look more like Dad than Mum.
But the guy who did this painting
made me look odder than I could manage by myself.
I mean my eyes and lips and nose are not that blistered!
My arms, honest, don't look like spider legs,
and my eyebrows look like an afterthought,
like the frantic underlining of a dinky signature.

Gran says, "Oh Jojo, my dear,
you belong to the hyphenated people,
the bewitching children of mixed parents.

Sure, aren't you the beautiful generation,
the future of the world?"
She insists I should be proud of how I look.
I mean, guys, if you looked like I look,
would you be dancing in the mirror?
Get real . . .

Mum decided to send me to Westminster School,
just next door to the Abbey,
and it's dead posh and expensive.
Some of the white lads there think I look weird –
"Muslim Paddy," some call me.
All my school friends are brown or black,
anything but WASP stings.
Oh, I know that when some people look at me
they think I'm a refugee crackhead
or some chickenhead peddling ecstasy in the playground.
I can see it in their eyes, marking me down.

Three years before I entered the school
I had to sit pre-interview tests
in Maths, English, and Reasoning.
After the interview I was awarded
a conditional place for when I was thirteen.
(Gran said: "Jesus, Mary and Joseph,
assist me in my last agony,
but what is conditional about you, tell me?")
Anyway, last June I did the Common Entrance exam
and passed with flying colours.
Mum and Dad were delighted and relieved;
Gran didn't raise an eyebrow at the news.

I love the school and most of the teachers.
Sporting activities are known as "stations"
and they have the usual public school stuff –

like squash and fencing and rowing –
but sadly, no skateboarding.
A bit too ghetto, I guess, for them,
just like I look.

I'm addicted to skateboarding, mostly street skating
on pavements, kerbs, benches, handrails, steps,
on anything that surfaces along the way.
I'm just about getting used to some moves,
now struggling with the frontside pop-shuvit,
basic stuff but difficult.
You put your right foot in the middle of the deck
and your back foot on the tail,
then bend your knees and start to jump
while hitting your tail to shove it around;
and as you watch your board rotate below you,
you catch it, to stop from over-rotating,
and when you land on the board again,
you keep your balance, then goofyfoot away.

Sounds easy, I know, but it ain't.
I'm getting the hang of it now
and Gran always cheers when I land right,
whooping it up like I've scored for Chelsea.
"Aren't you just great, Son!" she will shout.
"Aren't you just great!"
Nobody else thinks I'm great.
She's my *numero uno* fan –
well, to be honest, my only one.

And when I end up in a tangle of arms and legs and wheels
she'll pick me up and dust me down
and say, "Don't worry, Son, next time…"
I often wish I could see me like Gran does.
I mean when Gran looks at me I feel different,

sort of important when I look in her eyes,
and she beams from ear to ear,
making thousands of wrinkly lines
so that her face looks like Euston Station from the air.

Sometimes she calls me her little monkey –
guess who bought the tee shirt I'm wearing?
I have a wardrobe of tee shirts from Gran,
and my favourite has a pic of a skateboard on it
with the words, "Free Your Mind!"
Cool, I think.
I usually wear my rosary beads at weekends,
but they don't go with skateboarding
coz you could get snuffed doing a turn.

Poor Gran!
About three months ago I heard Mum and Dad
having one of their "little chats" in the kitchen,
and Mum tells Dad that she's started
to look for a "good home"
for Gran so she can be properly looked after.
I think Mum wanted Gran tidied away
in some disinfected villa on the Costa Geriatrica
where she could join the invisible people
who live their lives against a wall.
Dad was appalled at the very thought
and when he suggested that Gran
could come and live with us
Mum banged her hand on the counter
and stormed upstairs.

It reminded me of an incident a year earlier.
Pope Benedict – I forget the number he is –
made the Muslim world mad, including Dad,
about some quote he used from long ago

criticising what the prophet Muhammad
brought to the world.
Dad was apoplectic; Mum was defensive –
even though she has "lost the faith" as Gran puts it –
maybe, I guess, the pope is still important in her mind.
Mum and Dad didn't speak for two whole days,
instead appealing to the four of us for agreement.

How could we settle the argument?
I don't know about my three bros, but me,
I don't know who I am coz I don't know who to lean to:
a committed Muslim dad or a lapsed Catholic mum.
I don't feel, to be honest, I belong in either world
but have a sense that I'm a muddled refugee from both.
I'm in-between two different planets on a collision course,
and I feel an alien in my own place –
that's, of course, if I had such a thing as a place.

Hyphenated people like me find themselves
with a family, a postal code, and a country.
I have a British passport – or at least an EU one,
I forget which, since Mum always keeps it safe.
I go to an English public school
and benefit from the best education available.
But all this doesn't add up to a secure identity,
an awareness of self, a feeling of belonging,
a sense of being accepted for who I am.
Even though I have an address,
I don't feel I have a place, somehow.
I've got no "here" to belong to.

I don't know if this makes any sense to you.
I do know that Gran has a mega sense of herself –
I don't mean in any affected way –
and I really wish I had a dollop of that.

I also think that's one of the reasons
why Dad admires her so much.

I know Dad worships Gran, and Gran returns the favour –
Mum says they're a "mutual veneration society".
While Dad adores Gran just like I do,
I feel that Mum and Gran are poles apart.
Don't get me wrong: they love each other
in their own peculiar Irish way,
and they're always polite to each other,
though there never seems much warmth there.
Polite, yes, except the day Mum got angry
when she was taking Gran to the ballet at Covent Garden,
and when Gran came down the stairs in her usual outfit,
Mum exclaimed: "Oh, Mammy, you look like
you've assembled yourself deliberately
from the leavings of a jumble sale!"

I suspect Mum's a bit embarrassed by Gran's
holding onto the old familiar ways like she does.
Funny, I love Gran for that – she knows who she is
and she ain't going around apologising
or adjusting herself to fit in.
When Mum said that, in front of all of us,
Gran smiled, I remember, and said:
"Mary Frances, didn't I teach you to pass no remarks
on how people look or how they dress?
Sure doesn't it take all sorts to make up the world,
all sorts of people?" And she smiled again.
Mum's remark must have kicked Gran in the heart;
I really felt for her that day.

I know Mum loves Gran –
they are mother and daughter, after all –
although I've learned there's nothing automatic about love.

Last December Mum took me
to the Velázquez exhibition at the National Gallery,
explaining to me on the way
that cathedrals and churches were being supplanted
as places of gathering and pilgrimage
by art galleries and theatres,
by football stadiums and shopping centres.
I wasn't sure what she was saying.

After the exhibition, which I loved,
coz half the people in the paintings
looked like Gran overdressed,
we came out onto Trafalgar Square
and there was a black Gospel choir,
supported by three musicians,
singing Christmas carols
on a stage under the big Christmas tree.
It was a magical sight and sound, really festive stuff.
We were drawn
by the singing and the crowd and the applause,
so we moved over and stood
at the edge of the crowd to listen.
Some people in Santa Claus hats
were going around the crowd,
shaking their yellow buckets,
collecting for some charity.
The choir started to sing, in real slow tempo,
the carol "Away in a manger",
and by the time they started the third verse –

> *Be near me, Lord Jesus; I ask thee to stay*
> *close by me for ever, and love me I pray –*

I felt Mum begin to shake beside me,
and when I looked up tears were rolling down her cheeks,

like she had just heard real bad news
or just lost someone she'd always loved.

I'd never seen Mum cry before, and it scared me,
so I asked, "Mum, what's wrong?"
She gripped my hand and led me away
from the singing and the crowd,
away from whatever it was that touched her,
and her hand got tighter as we crossed the busy square,
through all the Christmas shoppers and the tourists,
and only when we passed Nelson's column,
and it got quieter did she say,
"Sometimes, Jojo, the past you thought was buried
comes suddenly back and scars the soul."

She hailed a passing taxi, and we travelled home in silence.
She never mentioned it again.
When I spoke about it to Gran that night, after her pipe,
she smiled at me and said, "Jojo, my dear,
you can't ditch your past like it's an old overcoat,
for it'll come back to wear you."

I'm not sure, to be honest, what she meant.

One thing I need to say to you:
the reason I leaked the secret about Gran and the pipe
is coz Gran died last week.
I tell her secret now – not to "expose" her
like some sanctimonious article in the red tabloids –
but to venerate her as the most self-made person I know,
"a real playa" as Sol called her.

We all flew over to Donegal for the "wake" and the funeral,
and Sol came with us, paying the fare from his pocket money.

"Yo," he said, "we just lost our gang leada.
Respect has to be paid.
Who we be real with now, bro?"
Hundreds of people shook my hands and murmured,
"Sorry for your trouble."
The Mass was packed out,
with people standing everywhere,
and all the shops in Creeslough were closed out of respect.
It was the saddest day of my life, saying goodbye to Gran
as she went upstairs for ever.

The parish priest said nice things about her
and Mum added a few thoughts at the end of the service,
but neither caught the spirit of Gran.
The four of us boys got to take up the offertory gifts –
wine and hosts and stuff –
but what I really wanted to carry up the aisle
was her old pipe, her rosary beads, and my skateboard.
I wanted to show everyone three things
that lifted Gran into another realm:
the rosary that was her chatroom with God,
the pipe that was her secret way of chilling out,
and my skateboard that made her whoop for joy.

(When I suggested this to Mum she told me not to be silly.)

But most of all, more than anything,
I'd like to have played her voice,
that soft-strong voice that launched me
on a thousand jumps
and soothed me on a thousand crash-landings;
the voice that made all my friends a bit more tolerant
for the awesome one-offness of its stubborn kindness.

Oh, believe me, her voice is in my head
for as long as I live in this demented world
and I'll never let it go.
And when they call me "Muslim Paddy" at school,
or "Saucer Eyes" or "Snake Lips",
I'll see Gran standing there beside me
in her old bonnet and coverall dress,
hugging me with her eyes,
whooping it up and shouting,
drowning out all other voices in the world:
"Aren't you just great, Son!
Aren't you just great!"

And I'll always remember that she trumpeted this
not as a question but as an exclamation.

Some nights now, when I feel lonely,
I slip into Gran's room and chat with her.
Her room's been redecorated –
the minimalist look I believe it's called –
and the Jesus figure has been packed away somewhere,
and her personal stuff has disappeared in black bags,
taken to God knows where.
What charity shop would want them?
How quickly, I thought, the remains of a life
can be tidied away…

When I go into Gran's room,
I kneel down by the fireplace,
hoping to catch the whiff of her clay pipe;
and when I'm down there I pray for her –
although I'm not sure who I'm praying to –
that if the God she loved so fervently
has so many rooms in his big mansion in the sky,
he might have a little attic, with a fireplace,

where Gran can hunker down and have a little puff,
to free her tired spirit.
I mean, she won't need her rosary no more.

Anyway, I'd better sneak back to my own room now
and leave this redecorated smokeless zone to itself.

Goodnight.

Or as Gran would say,
"Goodnight now."

Double Portrait
Giorgione

Looking back at yourself

For the director and staff of Galleria dell'
Accademia, Florence

You have to admit I look gorgeous!
Oh, by the way, I am known as Giorgione,
which is not the Italian for gorgeous,
but it might as well be, dear onlooker,
as I look dreamily, lazily, into your eyes.

My real name is Giorgio Barbarelli
and I was born in Castelfranco, a small town near Venice,
and it was to Venice I was sent, when I was fourteen,
to be trained under the artist Giovanni Bellini.
I was regarded as painfully beautiful,
exuding such a princely persona that my fellow artists
gave me the name of Giorgione, or George the Great.
Soon I became known as Giorgione da Castelfranco,
putting plain George on hold.

What you see is a double portrait
I did ages ago, dear onlooker,
of how I used to look when I was young
and how I came to look some years later:
you see the beautiful Giorgione gradually becoming
what he once was, plain old George.

Some critics think that the duo at the window
are a young aristocrat in front,
backed by his tutor in music –
a not-uninspired guess,
given what little the public knows of me.

Oh, I know they look like different people
from different social worlds,
and at first, I admit, I was relieved when most viewers
thought they actually were – different people, I mean.
Perhaps in some ways they are,
for we all change in distinctive ways;
sadly, as you know, we all forsake our better selves.

But now I confess to you, dear viewer,
that the double portrait is of me:
now you have it from the horse's mouth.
All right, since we are in confessional mode,
I admit I didn't want people to recognise me readily
so I painted my second self a little differently –
about ten years younger than I actually was at the time
while cropping the face and thickening the nose –
but I still tried to be modestly honest,
to myself at least,
in marking and masking the onset of decline.

You should see me now . . .

My younger self
is standing on a balcony of our palazzo
in what I thought at the time was a ravishing pose,
although I have to admit now that my right elbow
looks a bit daft suspended in the air like that,
but I wanted you to focus
on my sculptured Giorgione face,
so I painted the delicate little finger of my right hand
directing you to the arched eyebrows
and the eyes that are deep and watery,
like swimming pools, so deep you could lose your self.

The eyes are everything, don't you think?
Have you ever been fastened by a deliberate look,
dear onlooker, one that is made
without apology or resentment?
How can you resist that face,
and that bare, sloping, inviting neck?

I loved being looked at when I was young,
and wherever I went, people stared at me,
gobbled me up as I passed by,
admiring God's handiwork in making me,
or, it has to be admitted, just admiring me.
"God did not rush when making you,"
my mother used to say.
"God took her time to craft your loveliness,
fashion you as her special work of art."
(Theologically, Mama mia was way long before her time.)
Well, you know what mothers are!

From an early age
I knew I was attractive not only to women
but also to men,
and was free to choose
whatever fluttering presented itself.
Visitors would scurry to the palazzo
at all hours of the clock,
love's mad arithmetic crowding round the door:
they would stand outside
with stayed breath and new shoes,
then pull on the episcopal bell
to access their dream.
Papa would be furious and bark, "Wrong house!"
and complain about the hysterical fuss the groupies made,
but Mama only worried we'd run out of vases.

Oh, I did fall in love only once in my life;
early on, with a Venetian girl,
and was just about to marry her
when my best friend, whom I adored,
carried her off,
leaving me twice cheated, of love and friendship.
I was widowed before I was ever married,
and nothing and nobody has ever filled the absence,
I mean ever.

What happens when you give yourself,
body and soul and mind to another person,
believing that this one will be for ever inseparable
from you, for ever essential to your core identity?
You cannot imagine the dawning of a day
or the setting of the sun without *this one*,
and then, casually, without warning,
all the lights in your world go out
and you are left in crucifixion darkness.
How could you have misread things so badly?

After that, my heart was bolted.

Passion, once defeated, brings its own faltering clarity;
your hurt can make you wise – for ever.
Whoever has pleased me since, I have taken
with my catholic ambisextrous tastes,
one by one by one,
each one disinherited on arrival.
I would greet the newcomer with one welcoming eye
while the other eye was already fixed on exit.
My favourite line in all of Shakespeare's plays
is a stage direction: *Exeunt all.*

Since that breach of trust,
I've never met any lover twice:
repeated intimacy I came to regard
as a fanatic's pursuit.
As in the Church's extensive litany of the saints,
one name is announced at a time –
without repeat –
then greeted with the congregation's affirmation,
so my gathering of names, half-remembered,
has become the extensive litany of my life,
only never repeated with affirmation.
It gave me pleasure for a while, I don't deny it,
but the litany didn't add up to an alleluia of a life.

After my double trauma
I insisted that my heart,
such as it was, would never be for rent,
never be anyone's habitual ferryman
because I knew I couldn't keep
whatever traffic I picked up,
could only deliver them to the other side,
drop them off for their onward single journey,
then turn away.
And when they waved me from sight,
futile scribbles fluttering in the moonlight,
the instantaneous grief that came upon me
was always overtaken by relief in being alone again:
I was free again to reassemble myself, drift awhile,
wait for fresh winds
or the wink of another light,
then break for new horizons.

My life was touch and go.
What was it my psychiatrist said to me?
"The wounds you do not want to heal are you."

I have difficulty distinguishing.
Perhaps you have experienced this yourself, dear friend?
Have you ever, for example, driven to an airport
and while making your approach,
assaulted by all those signs,
have you ever had to pause,
just for a moment, to remember
whether to arrive at arrivals or arrive at departures?
Are you leaving someone behind you
or picking someone up?

Anyway, when I thought I was heading for arrivals
to pick up my stunning new Venetian wife,
she and my best friend had already made off
on their departure flights.
Since that day
I promised myself
I'd never be seduced by all the brisk promises
of amnesiacs whose appointment books
were in storage.

How many winds does it take
to blow away the waste of promises?

I had plenty of critics, more of my life than my work.
My way, they used to say, fostered leaving,
was sign of an old ineptitude for holding on.
Others said I dithered a life away
tyrannised by threshold,
scared of crossing into ambush.

One of my artist friends described me as "metrosexual"
and sent me this excerpt from a blog:

The typical metrosexual is a young man
with money to spend,
living in or within easy reach of a metropolis –
because that's where all the best shops,
clubs, gyms and hairdressers are.
He might be officially gay, straight or bisexual,
but this is utterly immaterial
because he has clearly taken himself
as his own love object
and pleasure as his sexual preference.

Whatever I am, I am. From the beginning,
I told people, as honestly as I could manage,
that my heart was not for hoarding people,
was never primed for lingering long,
never hungry for keepsake.
(The only memento I've ever known in my life
is a pressed pillow beside me
in the grey light of dawn.)
Sometimes, I told my once-only partners,
sometimes the only thing you can do
is smile at the gathering dark,
close the shutters,
draw the curtains
and bid yourself goodnight.

The swift phrase I heard repeated,
like a responsorial psalm,
was "See you again!" –
a phrase I never used myself
except to the two people I never saw again.
And I've always been wary of useless revelations,
especially to emotional burglars
who will steal everything from you
and leave you not a rumour of themselves.
Don't you think that those

who persistently press for information
must inhabit the dullest lives on earth,
borrowing ecstasy from passing strangers?
Whatever; but I did think that
what I disclosed about myself
might be *useful* as well as being true.

Anyway, I divert: back to what you see of me.
Just look at the quality and style of my clothes!
Look at that hand-woven lace shirt,
specially crafted for yours truly in Bruges
by a clever seamstress who travelled all the way to Venice
just to measure the dimensions of my neck!
Imagine!
And that black satin doublet
with the exquisite silk edging in gold
that was created specially for me, here in Cannaregio?
What do you think?
(Titian started going to my tailor,
but never did manage to achieve that limpid look.)
Sadly, you can't get a peek of my ankle boots from Florence,
each topped with a silver geometric buckle.

Gosh, that outfit cost my father a fortune!
He told me he could have bought
two thoroughbreds for the same.
But as one of your adverts bleats: "You're worth it!"
Which is why I believe that lust and eagerness
make for a deficient diet:
grace and style must surely be savoured.

And that wonderful mane of hair
to outshine any thoroughbred!
The work that went into contriving that avalanche of curls
that tumble down onto my shoulders!

My hairdresser used to come to the palazzo once a week
and work like an architect designing my head
to sparkle and shimmer
"and yet look casual", he would say.
I never did think he got the casual bit right.

And the pomegranate – not a wild orange as some think –
but *Punica granatum*, its crown
hidden as I hold it in my left hand,
which rests on the limestone window ledge:
what do you think?
Granatum means "seedy, abounding in seed" – that's me…
I'm told a large pomegranate holds
about eight hundred seeds;
when you cut it open you can see
the seeds surrounded by
scarlet pulp filled with juice –
all very bloody and delicious.

I'm sure you've seen the pomegranate
in medieval tapestries,
usually when the mythical unicorn's been captured.
Wild by nature, headed by a single spiral horn,
the unicorn, it is said, can be tamed only by a virgin.
Once restrained, it's held in an enclosed garden
and chained to a pomegranate tree.
So what tames the unicorn, I ask you?
Why does this wild animal become docile,
settling down and resting his horn
on the lap of a smiling virgin?
Which of them eats the pomegranates?

Oh, I have tried pomegranates,
eaten barrow-loads of them from the fruit market:
believe me, they don't induce stillness.

All right, I admit, that pose holding the pomegranate
does look artificial now,
but artifice was the style then:
every artist included a piece of fruit or a dog somewhere
in his painting to flaunt his skill
in drawing still life or animals.
So, big deal, I was a child of my time.
I have always, I admit, been drawn to artifice myself
because I've always had reason to believe,
more than most,
that reality is somewhat overrated.

That said, my painting holds me well, I think,
and has preserved my once-upon-a-time beauty intact,
showing me as youthful, beguiling,
refined, alert, unwrinkled.

But now, dear onlooker,
after all these years of passage,
only the balcony and window-frame remain unchanged,
except they now back onto a large loneliness
since the emptiness behind
has been up for sale for years.
Our palazzo, the backdrop of my prime, my family,
and my dreams,
is dispossessed,
all shuttered now, folded into itself.
Now it's become the kind of place
where only burglars call.

And behind me in the painting, there I am again,
with Mama's sky-blue water-silk
wallpaper as background.
What do you think?
You notice something strange:

my second self, standing in the window frame,
seems over-lit
while my younger self, balconied in full daylight,
is in part shadow.
That was a moment of honesty, for me,
conceding to the viewer
that, for all the prominence
my art gives to beauty and poise,
my younger self is already shifting into shadowland:
the real limelight has moved to my second self.

How can someone, once so beautiful,
become so commonplace, one of the invisible
you pass by in the street without a glance?
The stunning appearance has gone, so has the pricey outfit;
the self-assured look has vanished,
together with the attitude:
now, as you can see for yourself, the unexceptional prevails.
If anyone commented on my good looks then,
I knew they were reciting from memory.

So, I fell on hard times, dear onlooker,
and fewer and fewer people
were entranced with my art,
and fewer and fewer people
turned up to my exhibitions,
however well promoted they were by my rich padronas.

The major reason, I confess, was that Titian –
that clever pagan draughtsman –
overshadowed me and became the darling of the dealers.
Witness how Vasari ends his piece on me in his book,
Lives of the Artists:

> *Giorgione's death brought great sorrow…*
> *but the pain of the loss was made tolerable*
> *because of the accomplished students he left behind,*
> *especially Titian, whose work far surpassed*
> *let alone equalled what was done by Giorgione.*

See what I mean? Do you understand how I was reduced?

People's disinterest makes you grow old before your time:
if people thrive on attention, neglect ages you, believe me.
Or maybe people just got tired
of all the strutting and the posing.
Who knows why people become
weary of what once excited them;
why they cannot stay attracted
to what first enthralled them?
But who am I in all the world to complain of this?

Anyway, getting back to the painting, dear onlooker,
you have to admit that my second self's hair
still has a fighting edge to it,
although, as you can see,
I dumped the Dolce and Gabbana tam-o'-shanter
with its two discreet golden horns.
That hatless, shadowless look has nothing to hide,
but, it has to be said, nothing to swagger about either.
I've become more humble, less poised, less assured,
downward-looking into nowhere.
Given who I'd become
I could not meet your eyes – even then.

These days, I have to admit, I am back to being alone again
with no aspiring courtiers, no desperados ravenous for love,
no need to keep that extra toothbrush handy, just in case.
These days, nobody wants me as their trophy companion
at the Oscars or to deputise for the usual absence beside them.

And now?
What, you might ask, has become of me now?
Most people think I died from the plague in 1510,
when I was thirty-three years of age,
wanting to believe the popular myth
that fragile beauty is best remembered
when dismissed in violence.
That plague I survived like my earlier personal one,
but never announced my recovery, such as it was,
since I'd become seriously disfigured.
By then Giorgione da Castelfranco
had gone the way of all flesh,
and I was back to being plain old George again,
with one exception:
I still have the mind and hands of Giorgione.

How can I paint myself now and draft for you
the body's enfeeblement and
the soul's prolonged disappointment?
Oh, I know I could paint in number three me,
include the present me
somewhere behind my second self,
but that would alert the world to my old age.
I think not: you can take humility too far
and end up degrading yourself.

Don't misunderstand me, I beg you:
I'm not ashamed of myself now:
I am an old craftsman
who can catch flashes of glory
and sketch the gradualness of decline,
as I still do, here in Titian's workshop in Venice.
We made up again – Titian and I –
especially when he heard my solemn vow
that I'd never paint as Giorgione again.
As once people thought his work was mine,

so now people ascribe to him what I have done;
even the experts don't know
which "Titian" is a Giorgione.
But who can I tell, dear onlooker, and to what purpose?

No, I will never paint another canvas as Giorgione,
or paint what now looks back at me in the mirror.
I am no geographer of decay –
I will leave that, in time, to Rembrandt
with his fascination for mapping mouldiness.
It's just that I don't want to document
my own decomposition for posterity's sake.
We all want to put our best face forward, after all,
and keep it there for as long as possible: you agree?
In the art books, who knows, old George *redivivus*
might win out over young Giorgione *magnifico*,
and for me, that would be tragic revenge on my best self.

Look at my *Double Portrait* and absorb the detail:
look at me at the height of my glory,
and look at me as I leave glory behind.
Don't you think that's enough
of my measured frankness?

How about you, dear onlooker, how about you?
How do you measure your today
against all your yesterdays?
Who are you now over against who you've been?
If we all grow into refugees from what we've been,
what part of yourself would you want to keep?
And, more interestingly, what part of yourself
would you want to hide from view?

I mean, what self-portrait would *you* want to leave behind?
And what would it really tell us, the onlookers?

Why don't you create your own portrait
and I'll come and see it?
Go on, I dare you! I really do!
I can be your onlooker and will try,
as tenderly as I can,
to understand your portrayal of yourself.

And I will be happy to sit down,
as you have kindly done with me,
and listen to your reading of yourself,
hoping that, like me,
you might hint at a life beyond the frame.
Is that a deal?

Please feel free to phone or text me at the studio.
Just remember, though, the name is George.

La Reproduction Interdite

René Magritte

"Mirror, mirror, on the wall"

For Len Kofler, the staff, and the students of the
Institute of St Anselm

When we look in the mirror
our critical eye comes into its own,
educated from genesis for disapproval:
it takes over the business of appraising
what is presented to it.
Standing or sitting, when we look in the mirror
we submit to this eye and begin the ritual of repair,
honing in on what needs fixing,
adjusting to make good.

The mirror is the new confessional
in the age of image and appearance,
the place where we are both penitent and priest.
And like a good penitent we try to remedy
the flaws we acknowledge to ourselves:
the daily ritual begins in accusation,
striving earnestly for absolution.

So we squeeze this bit here, pull that bit there;
shave or groom, lather or gel;
we flatten or spike, smooth or ruffle.
Oh, how we tend and bend and mend
until we feel set for the gaze of others!
We are all verbs: utter stillness in front of a mirror
is reserved for the morgue.
When was the last time, dear onlooker,
you scrutinised yourself in the mirror
without adjusting something?

Finally, just before we go, we bless our reflection
with a cautious smile – shame about the teeth, I know –
and turn away, prepared to face a waiting world.

When you face yourself in the mirror, dear onlooker,
you do not see yourself as others see you.
It is physically impossible to behold yourself:
you see only a reflection of what you think
others might see when you are long gone
from attending to your reflection.

And you understand, instinctively,
how important your face is
in the delicate art of communication.
You appreciate that if there is a discrepancy
between what you say and how you appear,
that people will always believe their eyes
more than their ears. Gut-wise, people
listen to you more with their eyes
than with their ears. They believe you
or cancel you on sight.

When you see me looking in the mirror,
you see a visual conundrum:
you see me looking at myself turned around,
looking at the back of my head. Weird, isn't it?
What you expect to see is denied you;
you feel what you see makes no sense.

(How mobile and fluid are your senses?
Do you smell the snow falling on Ben Nevis?
Do you see the Mozart notes that ruptured your heart?
Do you taste the Kerengas rainforest in Sarawak?
Do you hear the buttered asparagus, now on your plate?
Do you touch the dream you loved last night?)

There's nothing wrong with the mirror
in the painting, I have to tell you;
it wasn't bought from a circus auction,
a throwaway from the hall of mirrors –
you know the place, I mean,
where there's all those "fun" mirrors
that distort your size and shape
and make people laugh at themselves?
People's ready laughter is, of course, in relief:
they know, for sure this time,
that they're not what they appear.

No, this is a regular mirror
that does its job adequately,
giving back what it receives,
reflecting what comes before it
as truthfully as possible.
You will have noticed that the book –
the French translation of Edgar Allan Poe's only novel –
which lies on the white marble mantelpiece
is reflected exactly as you would expect.

You see me reversed in the reflection;
you see the back of my brilliantined head – twice.
So, if the mirror is just a mirror,
what is it about me, you ask?

The mirror is not playing games,
I assure you, dear onlooker,
but is doing what it always does,
giving back what it receives,
reflecting as truthfully as possible
what others see.

Was it Socrates, the Greek philosopher,
who said "Know thyself"?

Was it he who argued that
wisdom begins in self-reflection,
the ability to mirror your real self
back to your thinking self –
not to become a stranger to yourself?
Was it he who argued
that to study the world beyond
the boundaries of your own life,
without first knowing your own topography,
was a wholly misdirected venture?

I'm not sure who it was,
for classical philosophy is not my subject,
and it never did capture my interest.
I am utterly grounded, earthed, located:
terra firma is where I live,
which is why I lecture in geography
here at the Sorbonne in Paris;
an expert in faraway places
with unpronounceable names.
My hobby, for the record,
is collecting rare antique maps,
which now decorate the walls of my study
and the margins of my dreams.

Geography is my passion, my life, my vocation:
out there is where I really live.
Perhaps this happened – who knows? –
because when I was a child I was never taken anywhere,
not even to the next town on market-day,
because my parents were always too busy
working day and night in our restaurant upstairs,
and they would never allow their only child,
apart from going to school, to travel alone.

I was their prized possession.

I escaped early, dear onlooker,
broke loose long before others do.
Some people wait for years and years,
and then, one day, not much different from the rest,
the prospect of eternity as endless now
hits them like a thunderbolt
and they protest the only way they can:
they leave now behind them.

One day when you are sitting in the garden
of your *petit château*, the sun doing its duty
shining on your two children
as they needlessly polish the new Mercedes,
and your husband is inside, stocking the drinks cabinet
for his soon-to-arrive business partners,
you slowly rise from your garden chair and,
without speaking a word to anyone,
turn away from everything you once hungered for,
walk out on everything you settled for,
everything you thought you'd settled into,
and you never come back.

More parents run away than children.
When I was fourteen, my mother ran away
and threw herself into the dark of the River Sambre,
leaving my father and me for ever behind her.
She chose another now, another eternity,
and it has taken me years to understand
the impulse that made her chuck everything.

I was a runaway child,
in a cautious way, though –
nothing permanently daring, like *ma mère*, about me.
No, I learned to deprive now of the present tense –
difficult, I agree, in a philological sense
but not in a psychological one, believe me.

I learned to travel in my mind's eye,
without leaving life or home.
I may like to shock, but I am a conformist;
I worship the mysterious from a safe distance,
so I journey to faraway exquisite places
displayed on the maps on my bedroom wall.
Where my childhood friends had posters of rock bands
or footballers or film stars on the walls of their rooms,
I had maps that acted as lavish wallpaper.

None of the places I travelled to in my mind
was a fantasy island or a remote planet
(I dislike science fiction):
everywhere I went was on a map
that could be pinpointed precisely
in longitude and latitude.

"Reality as fantasy," I hear a psychiatrist say.

Geography was the exit from my miniature world,
and from the view outside my window,
which was the back steps of our parish church,
Saint-Jacques-sur-Sambre,
and the cobbled street, at eye level, outside.
Geography was my passport
out of below-street level –
up, out and away
to magical places on the other side of the world,
the farther away the better.
The atlas of the mind
creates its own itinerary.

One day, I remember it well,
for it happened to be my fourteenth birthday
and my mother and father were busy upstairs
in the main dining room

serving a special dinner to welcome the new bishop.
The rain, I recall, was bouncing off the street outside,
and a small flood insisted on
inviting itself into my room,
so I opened up a copy of *National Geographic*,
my favourite magazine,
and within minutes I was transported from my bedroom
to the Solomon Islands:
there, after leaving Honiara behind me
and hiking through the lush forests,
I stood gazing at the stunning Mataniko Falls plunging
down into a cave full of stalagmites, swallows and bats.

Believe me, dear onlooker,
when I say I was there –
body, soul, and mind –
I was there.
Had the Angel Gabriel come to make an annunciation
that day, to mutter predictably, "Do not be afraid, Henri",
he'd have thought he'd come to the wrong address.

The real world had gone from me:
the back door of the church had vanished,
the wet cobblestones were no more,
the small flood into my bedroom
ceased to matter – for evermore –
and the polite laughter from upstairs
had long evaporated
under the dominion of the Solomon sun.

I've always had this strange ability
to be somewhere else
other than where I am.
I have a gift for absence.
While you may have heard
of the sacrament of the real presence,

this painting projects the shadow side of this truth:
the sacrament of the real absence.

This is why, dear onlooker,
in spite of the subject I teach,
you might be surprised to know,
that I rarely travel, anywhere.
I hate travel brochures, junk mail,
mocked-up to illustrate some fake paradise
that is designed to sneer at ordinary time
and the reader's home address.
I feel no need to face the hassle of airports
or the small humiliations of security
as they radar your modest belongings
and, with gloved hands, feel your body
and your apparatus
for weapons of minor destruction.

Not for me, all this waiting and rigmarole,
because I'm always somewhere interesting,
which is nearly always somewhere
other than the place I currently inhabit.
My mind has granted me a visa
for entry to every corner of our planet.

I do inhabit a lovely space, though,
living in expansive rooms
here in Paris, on the top floor
of a large apartment building,
in the sixth arrondissement.
I chose this place, I admit,
because of the high ceilings
and the commanding outlook it affords.
My friend who lives across the hallway –
a member of our intelligence service –
joked with me one day

when I asked her how her job was going:
she said that it was all about
"smoke and mirrors".

I've never heard such an exact *summa* of my life!

To get back to the painting of me and the mirror…
The painting reminds me of a work by Magritte
which depicts a pipe, with the letters underneath,
"Ceci n'est pas une pipe" – this is not a pipe.
And in case you missed the point,
the artist repeated the painting with the assertion:
"Ceci continue de ne pas être une pipe" –
this goes on not being a pipe.
If it were a pipe, you could smoke it…

When you look at the painting,
you think, don't you,
that I am looking into the mirror,
staring at what the mirror reflects?
First, you see me standing in the room
with my back to you, facing the mirror;
then you see what the mirror reflects:
the two images fail to connect as you expect them to.
Is this self-reflection or self-deflection?
You think that I am standing there in a black suit –
am I wearing a tie? –
staring at the back of my head.

Some people identify the figure as Edward James,
an English patron of the surrealists; not so.
It is I, Henri, who stand there,
but I am not looking in the mirror,
for I am focused elsewhere.
Just like the two ancients,
Abraham and Sarah.

Indulge me, please, for a moment, dear onlooker,
and imagine our ancestors in the faith –
not to say a few other faiths –
standing together, supported by stout walking sticks,
in front of a large mirror.
The have one hundred and sixty years between them.

Who they are
or who they will become
is not reflected in the mirror.

The mirror will inform them, without regret,
that they belong to the legion of the defeated
who have been thwarted by life and luck.
It is clear to the beholding eye
that they are finished with life and should,
without protest, humbly rehearse for death.
The two ancients could feel clobbered
by the teaching of that reflection:
the staggering arithmetic of wrinkles, alone,
would explain, even to the boneheaded,
why the cradle will stay empty for ever.

But Abraham and Sarah, like myself,
do not submit to the tyranny of the mirror.
The three of us, I am certain, would sympathise
with the millions of deluded people
who genuflect before the god of the mirror.
Worshippers of this god make untold sacrifices,
spending thousands of whatever currencies
to placate this exacting idol: a nip here, a tuck further down,
perhaps a bountiful extension – "Just right *there*, Doctor."
People are no longer concerned about their immortal souls,
only how they appear now.
Welcome to the new cathedral of cosmetic surgery
with its high priests and bizarre rites.

No, dear onlooker,
we need a kinder God
before whom we bow the head and bend the knee.

Abraham and Sarah are my unrivalled teachers,
because they don't submit to the fascism of reflection.
No, they are somewhere else, like me,
inhabiting starry, starry nights.
These two antiques are busy noting their countless offspring
who will be as numerous as the stars.
The stars, of course, dear onlooker,
are not reflected in the mirror:
the mirror never reflects your dreams.

Their son, Isaac – a word which in Hebrew
means "laughter" – is the ultimate protest
against the mirror. Go on, dear onlooker,
free yourself and laugh at the mirror:
do not buckle your body in homage!

Sometimes it's our faith and dreams
that tell us who we are, not the mirror.
Sometimes it's our perception of what we see
that is severely flawed and distorted,
not our faith or our dreams.
Our hope does not come from what we see,
but from beyond the range of the mirror's estimate.
Our dreams can be the most real thing about us:
they were about Abraham and Sarah;
they are about me.

Faith is a way of seeing.

No, dear onlooker, believe me when I say
that this mirror you see in the painting
is dutifully giving back what it receives,

reflecting as truthfully as possible what comes before it –
in this case, what *you* see of me.

You have noticed, I am sure,
that you and the mirror see the same thing:
the mirror reflects what *you* see, dear onlooker,
as, indeed, it struggles to do every day of your life.

I have turned my back on mere reflections:
that is the truth you see in the mirror.
I am at home, *chez moi*,
like Abraham and Sarah,
only in my dreams.

The Promenade

Fernando Botero

Food for thought

For Fr Mark Lesage and Estela Padilla

I just received a letter this morning
which began: "Dear Monsignore Portobello,
since my eyes were first favoured by the sight of you
processing up the aisle, on a visit to our cathedral,
I have dreamed, time and again, of being your cook
because I have never set eyes on a man
who so looks like he adores food,
and I know you would cherish my generous portions."

Have you ever received such a curious offer, dear friends?
I never realised I was so transparent in my affections,
and while the letter was kind –
written in English rather than Tagalog or Ilocano –
there were no references appended or indeed offered;
neither was there any hint of the quality of her cooking
or her own area of culinary expertise,
only emphasis on the acreage of her portions.
I presume she was talking
about the lavish spread of her servings
rather than speaking about her body mass.
Santo Niño, preserve us!

I was especially puzzled
because I didn't advertise a vacancy
in our colourful parish newsletter
which is produced by three wonderful graduates
who are studying graphic design at St Louis University.
The newsletter is now online, if you please,
and you can even download my weekly recipe
which uses only the best of local ingredients

(not much use, I agree, if you're in Greenland).
Sorry, I get diverted easily, dear friends:
if you look at my eyes, which tend to roam around
in their own orbits, you might understand
my trouble in staying focused for long.
I have a look of fixed bewilderment
which has always disappointed those who come
looking for priestly certainty.

Where was I? Ah yes, the prospective cook!
I didn't whisper a hint to our beloved parish council
that I was hungering after a chef for the convento,
nor to the Good Shepherd sisters whom I visit regularly,
to pick up some of their toothsome peanut brittle
and their succulent blueberry and strawberry jams.
From where did she get the idea that I wanted a cook?

You'd never guess, dear friends, would you,
just looking at me, fitted compactly into my clerical dress,
that I cook for myself!
Although cooking, I admit,
approaches something of a passion for me,
living as a missionary here in the Philippines
cooking for myself is counted as a cultural oddity.
The people are readily kind and forgive me,
of course, being a foreign priest,
making allowances for an Italian far from home
who has to have some little compensation
for being so removed from Mama's home-cooking
and the wondrous trattoria of Genoa.

Don't misunderstand me:
I am very partial to Filipino cooking.
I love chicken *adobo*, a delicious stew
cooked in vinegar and garlic with soy sauce flavouring.
Pescado al horno can take your breath away –

as indeed it did for the nuncio on a recent visit
when I cooked it for him and enlivened it
with an experimental blend of spices.
Sadly, His Excellency had to be chauffeured away at speed
to the Sacred Heart Hospital where they eventually calmed
his choking fits. Naturally, I followed as soon as I could,
armed with the holy oils if they were needed,
but His Excellency insisted on no visitors.
In case you might be interested, the dish in question
was red snapper sprinkled with breadcrumbs,
normally baked in a thick onion-and-pimento sauce,
though the ingredients of my electrifying sauce
that caused such an apostolic upheaval that fateful night
will remain for ever *sub secreto*.

Like Italians, Filipinos love family and eating,
and when I first arrived here as a young priest
I was delighted at how often they meet
and how well they eat:
apart from the usual meals we all have,
they have *merienda* – delightful little snacks –
like *halo-halo*, a mix of fruit, sweets, crushed ice,
milk, beans and sometimes ice cream.
I confess I don't care for *balut*, however,
a fertilised duck egg, boiled and eaten in the shell;
neither does the nuncio, I hear.

His Excellency did write me the briefest of thank-you notes
some weeks after his brisk departure,
to explain that anything remotely spicy
makes an explosive impact on his innards.
I haven't seen or heard from him since then, poor man,
and somehow I am given to doubt
if I will be nominated for the refreshments committee
for the upcoming papal visit in March.

Much of the cooking here is influenced by
three hundred years of Spanish rule;
the Americans have contributed little, I have to say,
apart from McDonald's and that chicken grandfather
who hails, I think, from Kentucky;
but in fairness they were largely responsible
for setting out Baguio way back in the 1900s
as the summer capital of the country.
By the way, in case I forget to mention it,
my very favourite sweet dish is *ensaymada*,
stuffed pastries covered with butter, sugar,
and shredded cheese. Too heavenly for words!

Living here in Baguio,
in the beautiful Province of Benguet,
we live at an elevation of about 1500 metres,
so happily it's cool when the rest of the country is frying,
and we have no need of air conditioning –
that is why so many flock here for the summer
and our congregation doubles in size.
It's always a pleasure to welcome people
from all over the Philippines and from abroad,
and we have the most energetic welcoming committee
of any parish in the Catholic world.

Perhaps I should say at this point
that I have very little to do in the parish
except to be nice to people, which is no trial,
since the Filipinos are the gentlest people in the world
and, like me, they avoid confrontation at all costs.
Our parishioners do everything, even the preaching!
(Not a hint, please, to His Excellency about this,
otherwise I will be in receipt of headed notepaper
from the Vatican with unyielding warnings underneath,
overstamped with canonical insignia.)

The good Lord, in his ineffable wisdom, did not bless me
either with an interest in theology
or a gift for public speaking;
this is not a problem for me, however,
because we have a host of parishioners
who have degrees in theology and religious education,
and who preach magnificently every week
and oversee all the sacramental programmes.

My life and the life of the parish were changed for ever –
it now seems an aeon ago, looking back –
by a visit from two wonderful people
who came from Las Piñas in Manila,
Father Mark Lesage and Miss Estela Padilla.
Before their visit I tried to do everything in the parish –
preaching, planning, preparing for sacraments,
accounts, choir, social outreach, sick people, ecumenism –
you name it, I was doing it all by myself;
a one-man clerical industry
striding around "my parish" like a lonely Colossus.

Mark and Estela taught me to share and to shift,
to dump my messianic pretensions over a Baguio cliff,
and to recognise the talents sleeping in the people.
It was like hearing the Gospel for the first time!
Over a number of weeks, we called the parishioners
together in small groups, to challenge and trust them
to share ownership of the parish –
it is their parish, after all, not mine –
and the people took to their new ownership
like the famished to one of my simple suppers,
tinolang tulya – a ginger-flavoured mussel stew,
served with a garnish of spinach.
Oh, I know, dear friends, when people first see me,
they think I must be chaplain to Noah's Ark

(what did you think when you first saw me?)
but I am the most liberated parish priest in the world!

Apart from saying Mass, all I do is cook, really,
and visit those who are sick and housebound;
but I never eat dinner alone – can't remember when I last did –
because I always have a family from the parish
or a little group of parish workers over for a little platter,
and it's always a privilege and great fun to serve them.
They are forever asking me for the recipes,
so we are going to produce a parish cookbook next year,
designed by our clever graphic artists –
Agbayani, Buñag, and Macalosa –
with the voluptuous recipes written by yours truly.

Every night the people come – there is not a family
in the parish who have not relished my cooking!
We talk and eat, and laugh and eat, and drink and eat!
(The parish hospitality committee, God bless them,
ensures that everyone is invited, and after ten years
we are on our second round of helpings.)

The people of the parish were truly brave-hearted
when Baguio was struck with that killer earthquake
back on 16 July 1990 – the temblor, if I remember,
registered 7.7 on the Richter scale.
For so many nights after, we all huddled in tents
and makeshift shelters in the streets and the parks
because we were scared it might happen all over again.
So many people lost their lives,
including Marianna, my beloved cousin, and Roberto,
her husband, who had kindly come from Torino
to visit me on their annual two weeks' holiday;
they were killed when the Nevada Hotel
was ripped apart and collapsed in the quake.
May the good Lord have mercy on their souls.

It was the worst of times, bringing out the best in people.
With the three main roads into Baguio totally impassable,
we had to fend at first for ourselves, and the parish
set up a soup kitchen and shelters
where we were busy for days
scratching around for anything we could find to make stews
for the legions of hungry and homeless people.
We were warned to boil the water and cook the food well
because of the threat of typhoid fever and cholera.
If I wasn't cooking or boiling water, I was burying the dead,
many of them dear friends who had shared our table,
unburdened themselves a little in the candlelight,
unveiled their fragile dreams, and laughed at silly stories
into the reaches of the night.

I remember the night of the quake, it was a Monday,
when Maria, who plays the cello at the Masses on Sunday,
came stumbling to see me. She had nearly died giving birth
to her only-born child – I was there in hospital at the time –
and now she held the crushed body of her dead son
in her arms, holding him up to me like a broken promise,
asking, "Why, Monsignore, why?"

What words could I say that would make any sense?
I stretched out my arms and lifted her dead son
from her enfolding embrace,
carried him inside the convento to our big kitchen,
laid him down on the huge pine table,
and together, wordlessly, we washed the tiny body,
cleansed the wounds as tenderly as we could,
each signing the holy oil on his forehead and hands.
We then wrapped the body around in bath towels
and I carried him into the church, which was filled
with people praying, and laid him down
before the high altar.

I shall never forget the sight as long as I live.
The little boy's name was Angelito,
and he lay there like an angel fallen from flight,
too late for the Christmas crib.

Some women came up and gathered Maria in their arms
and sat her down on the front pew
where they held her and rocked her back and forth
like she was their wounded child,
breathing out the sighs and sounds of heartache,
joining the inarticulate groans of grief,
the growing lamentation heard throughout the city,
and beyond, throughout the land of the Philippines,
eventually becoming one with the huge chorus of sorrow
that cries from every corner of the world.

We prayed the ancient Latin prayer of departure:

> *In Paradisum deducant te angeli,*
> *in tuo adventu suscipiant te martyres,*
> *et perducant te in civitatem sanctam Jerusalem.*
> *Chorus angelorum te suscipiat,*
> *et cum Lazaro quondam paupere*
> *aeternam habeas requiem.*
>
> > *(Into Paradise may the angels lead you:*
> > *on your arrival may the martyrs receive you,*
> > *and bring you to the holy city of Jerusalem.*
> > *May the choir of angels receive you,*
> > *and with Lazarus, once a poor man,*
> > *may you have eternal rest.)*

Why is it, I asked myself that night,
that it's always the poorest people in the world
who seem to be God's favourite victims?
Why are the little people crushed so regularly by nature,
in floods, in earthquakes, in tsunamis?

I wouldn't want to endure that time again even as purgatory.
It takes a long time, even for a long-suffering people,
to sleepwalk back to routine life again:
the pain lingers long after
the demolition has been completed,
the debris swept up, the buildings repaired or rebuilt,
and everything is shimmering in the sun.
It takes a long time to let go of the dead,
leave them to rest in peace and turn to life again.

Thank God, we're all back to normal now
and we pray we will never be visited again
by the savagery that only nature can produce.
I also thank God that I was useful in a practical way.
Every day, if it is not raining, I take an afternoon stroll
on the Baguio Mountains, to my favourite spot
which is bare of any pine trees, and there I say the rosary
for dear Marianna and Roberto,
for Maria and Angelito,
for all the victims of that earthquake
and for those who died the following year
in the ashes of Mount Pinatubo.

When I think of that earthquake time and our soup kitchen,
when everyone was equal in their desperation,
I think of Jesus ministering to the five thousand,
and see that crowd of hungry followers satisfied
by the little his disciples could share with them.

I am not given to pious thoughts –
my daily breviary tends to be *Best Food Guides* –
but I think that Jesus got it right when he made
open table-fellowship the mark of his ministry,
infuriating all the religious snobs
who built enclosures around their dinner tables
so you needed a visa to sit down.

I love the bit in the Gospels – unsure where it is exactly –
where Jesus compares himself to John the Baptist:
the good Lord says that the Baptist comes not eating bread
or drinking wine, whereas the Son of Man comes
eating and drinking, and everyone calls him
a glutton and a drunk, a friend of sinners.

While John's disciples are set apart by prayer and fasting,
Jesus' disciples are identified by constant eating and drinking.
You have no idea, dear friends,
what reassurance that passage gives me!

Given John the Baptist's diet of locusts and wild honey,
you wouldn't be stampeding into the desert,
would you, for lunch al fresco!
I wonder if my prospective cook would ever
apply to John and fill him out with generous portions?
(If we went on a parish pilgrimage out into the wilderness
I think we'd pack a little hamper, to sustain us for the day,
with a few bottles of San Miguel Pale Pilsen,
a cool golden lager with a pleasant, clean, hoppy finish.)

And the Baptist's wardrobe, like mine,
inclines towards the eccentric – he wears animal skin
held together by a leather belt! Wild!
I am tamer by comparison, as you can see,
and go around every day in clerical dress
looking not unlike a midget advert for a theatrical costumier.
Believe me, I would look even more ridiculous
in another outfit.
The kids in our school think I look like the Infant of Prague,
so they've nicknamed me Santo Niño, the little devils!

My outfit comes from the Gammarelli emporium –
just off the Piazza Minerva in central Rome –
no ordinary tailors these, but outfitters to the popes.

Where else could I buy my *capello romano*,
my flat-brimmed clerical hat, with added purple edging
and that delicate little purple pompom
to match my monsignorial sash around my waist?

And since, dear friends, I wear a variation
of the same old regimentals every day,
I think I might as well have quality, don't you?
I mean, for instance, which of you would settle for a hamburger
when you could come home to me and have my *gnocchi al resole*
with a witty sauce of ground sausage, oyster,
mushroom slices, tomato and basil?

Our life is so fragile, and it can be cancelled so quickly,
that we might as well indulge our little foibles:
without them, how would God recognise us?
This truth I have been taught by the Filipino people,
who teach me in a week more about living the Gospel
than I ever learned during six wearisome years in a seminary.
Voce di popolo, voce di Dio –
the voice of the people, the voice of God.

Sometimes, I have found, the best education
is borrowing the eyes of others,
to see as they see – particularly the poor people
here in the parish whose way of taking in the world
is educated by a heart of tenderness and ready pity
that is, without doubt, treasured by the good Lord.
To look at the world all by yourself, dear friends –
as I used to do at the beginning of my ministry –
can be such a cheerless and crotchety affair:
it can wreck your head, leaving you a lonely snob.
Wasn't it St Catherine of Siena who said
that we should never look at ourselves alone,
for alone we are always in bad company?

Since I am not svelte, nor ever have been,
nor, in God's gracious providence, am ever likely to be,
my monsignorial robes cover my capacious self
with as much decorum as can be managed.
That umbrella was bought online from Milan
as a birthday present from our dramatic society
who wanted it to match the dome of my hat, they said!
It does look a bit bizarre – like carrying around
a black mushroom stool – but weren't our budding artists
resourceful as well as kind-hearted in choosing it?
You see it's shaped like a little rotunda?
I suspect they wanted it to mirror my outline…

I am the most recognised priest in Baguio –
everyone knows me and chats with me –
especially when I walk down Session Road
every morning after Mass, to head for my favourite destination,
Baguio City Market, a wonderful sanctuary of fresh produce
from the farms around Benguet,
such as fresh strawberries, tomatoes, lettuce,
mushrooms, broccoli, cabbage, Baguio beans –
the edible litany goes on and on, alleluia,
not to mention the array of fresh flowers!
They all know me there, of course, and some must think
that I'm buying for the army barracks or a catering college
with all the stuff I purchase from them;
but in friendship we have no need to bargain with each other.

Now, where was I? Ah, yes, Jesus and table!
(You can see why I rarely preach, dear friends, can't you?)
Anyway, because of Jesus' indiscriminate welcome
to all sorts of weird and wonderful people,
he got himself into the most dreadful trouble
with the hierarchy of his day, those old religious fusspots
who couldn't tell their *agnello* from their *vitello*.

These old sticklers thought they got the upper hand
when they dumped him on the killing fields.
But before he handed himself over to his enemies,
he handed himself over to his friends
as they gathered for their Last Supper.
At this meal, he said, he was the menu,
offering himself with the lovely words:
"Take, eat, this is my body, given for you.
Take, drink, this is my blood, shed for you.
Do this, and remember me."

And the Good News is that Jesus maintains
his unfailing welcome to all of us, to this very day,
making himself food and drink,
"for you and for all" as the good prayer says.
I am glad I follow the one who came into life
in Bethlehem – "the house of bread" –
in a borrowed feeding trough for animals
and, at the end of his life,
at the borrowed table of a dear friend,
would leave himself behind as sacred food and drink:
a broken body for a broken people.

Bread at the beginning; bread at the end.

My life, dear friends, is a movement between two tables,
between the morning table of the Lord
and the evening table of the people,
and I can see little difference between them.
Nor, as long as I live, do I ever want to;
nor ever, I pray, be left with only one.

Logo for Frankfurt Book Fair, 1998

Artist Unknown

Facing the truth

For Richard Golding

"Have a gander at this, Susan!" I said.
"What do you think? You like the outfit I have on?"
I asked my niece, hesitantly, when I placed
this drawing, made of me for the Frankfurt Book Fair,
on her unexploited breakfast table.
This was two weeks ago, in Belfast.
"Hmmmm," she said cautiously, glancing down,
"you want tea or coffee? Maybe juice?
I've got pineapple, orange, blackcurrant."

She's a neuro-clinical psychologist,
with a speciality in brain injury,
unthrilled by breakfast consultations on the sly.
After the fuss of pouring an unwanted cup of tea –
time to think, I suppose –
she said: "Your outfit might look good under special lighting,
say on a designer's walkway at midnight,
you know, when the champagne is flowing rivers
and judgements are veering off the compass;
but, otherwise, under normal lighting in Tesco's,
your outfit does, I have to say,
lean towards the ostentatious
on a man,
Uncle T."

I felt like Jacob, limping away,
hip-socket newly dislodged,
brain out of joint,
after mistakenly wrestling with God:
down but not out...

Leaning over the sink, with her back to me –
not her usual stance, I guess, for one-to-one –
she said, "Don't mind me asking this, Uncle T,
but are you a cross-dresser or something?
I mean that's fine; it takes all sorts to people a map.
I love books – art, fiction, even some religion –
but normally we don't wear them as our wardrobe.
To a casual observer your outfit might appear garish,
but I know a fine psychiatrist who could wean you back
to wear what most of us might agree as normal gear."
Finishing at the sink, she turned around to ask,
"How's the tea?"

Let me explain, if I may, dear stranger.
Once upon a time – I have been around for aeons –
way back before alphabets and cuneiform,
I used to walk everywhere naked, totally starkers.
I was Truth, and never felt the need for clothes,
never mind being weighted with a library.
I was Naked Truth, crisp as honesty,
unencumbered and undisguised
as truth, I believed, should be.

How I loved to go for long hikes, always solo,
breathe in clean air, mountain-fresh,
and feel at home in nature's refined rawness;
but when I came near to human habitation
and met people coming up the road towards me,
on seeing me they'd scarper, head for the hills
to confide in the heather rather than in me.

Sometimes, if my path took me through a village
and I walked down the main street,
everyone would suddenly scurry away,
like the possessed fleeing the chartered exorcist,
into the fastness of their houses.

Such a fit of activity you never saw outside the Olympics!
They would scramble to lock, fasten, secure, bolt, bar –
all to keep out the one they called
"the wacky streaker".

Never mind Special Forces,
I could clear a street in a matter of seconds.

This did not, of course, dear stranger,
nourish my self-image or soup my soul;
rather, it felt as if I had a communicable disease,
like a plucked turkey with H5N1 avian bird flu,
so that people felt compelled to stay away from me
as if advised by the Health and Safety brigade.
I mean, all I wanted to do was have a blether,
sit down with people, together as friends,
and share the insights we'd gathered on the way.

I don't know if you've ever had the experience
of habitual rejection,
of people instinctively rebuffing you
even before you could utter a word?
They hate the way you smile
or the way you're dressed
or the circumference of your hips,
or the way you blow your nose
or the way you fold a napkin.
Who cares? Anything will do.

With me, it was my nakedness;
but I wanted to explain to people that
Naked Truth was who I was,
the very nature of me, my soul, my self,
my sum, my substance, the quintessence of me.
Why could I not be myself with them?
Or was it, perhaps, they feared
they could not be themselves with me?

I ended up lonely, the reluctant outsider,
an outcast with no companionship,
muttering away to myself
like some daft old country bachelor
wandering the lanes at night,
chasing long-lost ghosts.
My only game was Solitaire.
I used to think to myself,
having only myself to think to,
that I'd end up demented, certifiable.

One evening, when I was quitting a village,
leaving everyone in lock-up behind me,
I saw Story approaching down the road.
Oh, she did not strain the eyes,
dressed in fashionable sumptuous clothes,
like she was heading for the King of Hearts' ball.
I'd heard of her, of course, who hasn't?
I'd heard that when she smiled on you,
you felt, of all humanity, you were the most blessed.

She had collected, everyone knew this,
the most extensive wardrobe in the world,
with a change of get-up for every conceivable occasion.
Alongside that, she had a centipede's lust for shoes
that would leave Imelda Marcos
looking like a discalced Carmelite!

Story was, I admit, stunningly attractive.
"How d'you do?" she said, proffering a hand.
"How d'you do?" I replied, taking it.
Civility done, she shook my hand warmly,
even affectionately, as if I were an old familiar,
all the time keeping custody of the eyes –
she had been brought up by the nuns, I heard.
She quickly moved to the heart of the matter.

"What is the matter with you?" she asked.
"You look so depressed and disappointed.
Tell me what's wrong."

I told her frankly (how else can I talk?)
that nobody wanted me, nobody accepted me.
"When people see me coming," I explained,
"they scamper and hide until I've gone."
"Imagine," I said, "when you were a child
playing hide-and-seek, and it's your turn to hide,
so you choose this clever place to go to ground,
but then you realise, after an age has passed,
that nobody's looking for you?
Everyone quit a long time ago."

I looked at her and said, "This I know for sure:
nobody's looking for me and I can't find anyone.
You're lucky, always being invited into people's houses,
called upon, looked for, pressed to sit down
and share their family meals and stories.
People love you; they sit around
hanging on your every word.
Why does everyone avoid me?"

"May I act out of character
and be totally candid with you?" Story asked.
"Please do," I said, "I'd appreciate that."

"Everyone avoids you," she said, "because of who you are.
Who wants to sit down and share with Naked Truth?
Who wants to see themselves through your eyes?
You are too much, like an unforgiving mirror,
so people take cover as soon as they see you.
I'm sorry, Truth, but, believe me, that's the truth.

"You live inside your enclosure of clarity,
looking out in disapproval at the fog of humanity.
You want to clear things up, spell out, resolve,
shine your unrelieved light on everything in sight,
dismiss the shadows from the human story.
'Tell it like it is!' is your credo, in need of nuance.
You want to demolish all our hideouts,
leaving us without a sanctuary to hide our shame.
But I doubt if you've ever entered anyone's real world
of ambiguity, confusion, and darkness.

"Life is untidy, believe me," Story said, "it's arbitrary;
life is too much to stare at for too long.
You should remember a delicate observation
from Cardinal Jean-François de Retz:
'One abandons a sense of ambiguity at one's peril.'
Since Adam and Eve the history of the human race
has been steeped in ambiguity and uncertainty:
you must remember how the first human beings
hid parts of themselves from each other
and the whole of themselves from God:
cover-up was their first natural instinct.

"By now, dear Truth, you surely know
that the human story is mostly lived in camouflage,
lived out in the language of dissimulation.
Life is an agreeable masquerade
where all the masked players know the rules.
And you, Truth," she said, "walk around
like some noble exception, totally exposed,
feeling no need for anything
as common as a fig leaf.

"Why don't you use a bit of imagination?" she asked.
"I really don't want to be hard on you, Truth,
but if you carry on the way you are,

you'll end up in an asylum somewhere,
in some isolation cell, screaming at the bare walls
with yourself as cloistered audience.
Honestly, you will.

"Or you will end up like some mad Icarus
who flew too near the sun
because he thought he could be at home
in the untempered heat and light.
You are a serious age now," she said.
"You must have learned some caution along the way.

"I'll tell you what," she said, changing her tone,
"let me make some clothes for you
and then we'll see how people respond.
I bet you, life will change for you,
and you'll become a new man;
you won't even recognise yourself.
Go on, be adventurous, give it a try!"

I was reluctant to accept Story's advice,
but, to be honest with you,
I was so exhausted,
utterly weary of being excluded from normal life,
that I decided to risk it.

Two weeks later three parcels arrived,
courtesy of Securicor.
It took me ages to assemble myself –
clothes, after all, were never my thing –
and when I discovered which bits go where,
I managed to dress myself
in the clothes Story had made for me.
(Yes, that's me in the painting, dear stranger –
Truth dressed as Story –
trying out a few new moves.)

At first I felt strange and itchy,
all covered up, with only the safe bits showing.
I practised walking in front of a mirror,
absorbing my new self from every angle,
analysing every move and turn
like a novice dancer practising
a new routine at the Royal Ballet School.

It took a long while before I felt natural,
at ease in this new outfit.
I didn't go outside for days
but stayed rehearsing before the mirror
how I might best appear in public.

To my delight, however, I discovered
that when I did venture out,
the plague had somehow disappeared:
people no longer avoided me,
but opened their doors
and welcomed me into their houses.

Oh, you have no idea
how that made me feel,
connecting, at last, with people!
While you do this every day, dear stranger,
without so much as a dedicated thought,
for me this was wholly novel.

I have been in this rig-out for long,
and now I have a litany of friends,
many followers,
many mimics,
even, it has to be said,
some impersonators.

I like who I am, the new me,
please don't misunderstand me;
but in the last couple of months
I'm beginning to wonder
what I lost on the way.
To be honest, dear stranger,
I'm no longer sure,
even though life is easier,
that I did the right thing.

People are so used to me now,
the decorated truth,
knowing only the dressed-up version of me,
that I wonder, when I listen to them,
if they can see beyond the dance
of my latest verbal shifts –
how I turn and spin and prance and weave,
to entertain, to inform, to delight.
Many people, it has to be said,
especially the young, have no memory
of how I used to be.

To be honest with you, dear stranger,
I'm beginning to think I'm a fake.

You understand that although I tell things differently now,
I still recognise things as they are;
I notice everything, catch every nuance,
observe every twist and turn,
absorb the clutter of detail.

I cannot help but mark the casual way –
how this happens every day of the world –
that the wretched of the earth are still mauled and bullied,
tortured and wasted, made to disappear,
catapulted into eternity without reason or cause.

And, apart from a few attentive journalists,
there is little moral fuss about their fate.
"Compassion fatigue" has become the fashionable illness
in the face of unrelieved tragedy.

I watch children being blown to pieces
as they walk to school,
their lives for ever cancelled,
just for being there, at that moment,
on that minor road without signposts.

The precision weapon, you understand,
that was aimed at the military installation
two miles up the road
landed in a pram being wheeled by two children,
blowing the three wanted children into the hereafter.
And the response?
"Our intelligence was the best available to us;
we took every precaution, as we always do,
and we profoundly regret any collateral damage."
Somewhere, someone once said:
"In war truth is the first casualty."

The remains of this tragic scene
are beautifully photographed, then cropped precisely
for the magazine you pick up in the hairdressers.
Not, of course, magazines like *Hello!* and the like,
celebrity chasers, who give you knife-edge titles like:
David and Victoria take time out in Nice;
Easy living is in the bag for Jessica's pet pooch –
I joke not. All this is accompanied
by leaden photographs of privilege
to underline the weightlessness of the reader's life.

(Never buy a magazine, dear stranger,
with an exclamation mark in the title.)

How you wish these witless editors
might read their Shakespeare – that Catholic genius
who put everyone on the stage: deranged kings,
perceptive fools, monstrous daughters, obese comics,
tender torturers, thoughtful thieves –
the list goes on for ever, reflected in the hunger
of so many who learn English to understand the Bard.

The wonderful lines in *Richard III* speak to me:

> *Because I cannot flatter and look fair,*
> *Smile in men's faces, smooth, deceive, and cog,*
> *Duck with French nods and apish courtesy,*
> *I must be held a rancorous enemy.*
> *Cannot a plain man live and think no harm*
> *But thus his simple truth must be abus'd*
> *With silken, sly, insinuating Jacks?*

Why is simple truth abused?
Why do we divert ourselves
with programmes claiming to be "reality TV"?
People on couches sit down
to watch other people sitting on couches,
and this passes itself off as reality.
Who wants to hear the truth –
except the little people?
But they are always the victims.

They only matter as cumulative digits
when someone wants a body count:
from morning to evening news,
mounting figures always impress
because we love arithmetic,
the distance of the calculator.

And on television, the reporting of these tragedies
is interrupted by a message from the sponsors,
advertising their wares, obliging happiness.
The drivel of scented words goes on and on
while the round of sadness
is like an everlasting rosary
of sorrowful mysteries.

Half the world lives in Gethsemane;
the other half is asleep.

Who can unearth the truth,
undress the reasons that are proffered,
starkly tell the story of what really happened
that morning under "friendly fire"?
Can people really see what's out there,
what lies beyond the borders of their restricted world?
Or are people damned to recreate the world
into the way they innately think,
into a homely adjunct of themselves?

You notice how a grave security threat
suddenly becomes a danger to civilisation;
citizens who object become traitors
or are branded "enemies of the people";
the judicial system is bypassed.
And most people go about their business:
life, after all, must go on.

W.H. Auden caught it well when he wrote
about how the Old Masters observed suffering:

> *In Brueghel's Icarus, for instance: how everything turns*
> *away*
> *Quite leisurely from the disaster; the ploughman may*
> *Have heard the splash, the forsaken cry,*

But for him it was not an important failure; the sun shone
As it had to on the white legs disappearing into the green
Water; and the expensive delicate ship that must have
  seen
Something amazing, a boy falling out of the sky,
had somewhere to get to and sailed calmly on.

Have I joined the litany of people
who turn away "quite leisurely from the disaster"?
I mean, do you think
it's time for me to dump the clothes
and return as my real self,
as Naked Truth?

Oh, I know I would not be wanted now –
never have been, I suppose –
but am I needed in some places?
I think I could bear the arctic loneliness
and walk the Via Dolorosa
with no cameras recording every step,
no disciples over my shoulder,
no journalists attending every word.
Just a few hurt women trailing in my wake,
processing behind me
lonely for the truth to be told.

Maybe my niece is right
and I should see that psychiatrist
who might wean me back to what, for me,
would be my normal gear – myself.

I mean, dear stranger,
if I may be personal and direct,
would you accept the real me?
Would you let me into your life
without the fancy wardrobe?

Villa on the Sea
Lionel Kalish

Stillness

For Julia Kerr

I have travelled the world
but never witnessed such stillness as this,
like a vacated monastery flushed by silence.
Your eye moves from stone to sea to sky
in the clutch of silence:
can you hear the hush?

Have you ever chanced on a sea so unruffled,
so like a vast ice-rink, glazed to luminosity?
Don't you feel you could glide with Jesus
along this surface with no need to hold his hand?
You see no wave, neither rise nor fall,
no lapping against the shoreline;
nothing so defiant as a splash against stone.

Utter stillness drawn tight as a drumhead,
a sea so pacific that it makes its larger namesake
a lustful tsunami, sexual fury as water.

The trees have caught the mood,
unbending in the breezeless air:
they stand motionless, like guards on duty
awaiting inspection – guards who know that a wink
or a shiver would be interpreted as an uprising.
The trees take their cue from the winged lion,
who has sat on this plinth for centuries:
in spite of the scrolled swagger of that tail,
what you see is monumental passion fossilised.

Could this be the lion from the Book of Daniel,
one of the four beasts that appeared in the prophet's dream
in the first year of the reign of Belshazzar, King of Babylon?
In the vision of the night the prophet saw
the four winds from the ends of the earth stir the great sea,
and behold – he wrote the dream down –
"the first was like a lion with eagle's wings"
which rose out of the sea and was given a human heart.

No fallen angel this, but a beast from below.
Is this where he landed, intending only to dry his wings
before taking off on some beatific mission?
Perhaps the new heart-transplant took fright
and he stayed put, petrified to move on?

Did he ever dream, I wonder, of the lion's heart
he lost for ever in that flawed exchange?

When you look at this headless sentry,
still looking dead alert, don't you just dream
of being there the day the lion lost his head,
so you could see and hear a real splash?
Gosh, what a riot that must have been!
Or, do you think the fall was soundless, unseen,
and so went unreported?

Do you think the air is circulating in this setting
unbeknown to us, or is it on hold?
The pearl-grey sky gives nothing away,
and cannot be called as a witness;
it gawks only at its own reflection in the sea
like some sedated washed-out Narcissus.
So together these two, even though they never meet,
they give and take, each to the other, endlessly –
the sky is over-salted and the sea is stippled pink:
you wonder what they're scheming.

No people here: no naked violinist at an open window,
not even the vestige of a human shadow;
no birds to sweeten the inscrutable sky
or household pets to indicate a hand that feeds;
no boats tied up, unfussily, upon that domestic landing;
no sign of comings or goings,
no children's toys lying around lazily
on the steps or the stone landing, as you might expect.
No indication of a neighbourly presence,
no silhouette even on the horizon.

Just that Romanesque archway into the dark,
its equilibrium mismatched in two steps.

That iron bracket, jutting out from the top balcony,
pestering you to notice its emptiness:
did it once bear a cardinal's coat of arms,
or perhaps hold a sign for this exclusive restaurant?
Or did people come here once on pilgrimage, in gondolas,
to see the Madonna of the Robe?
Do you think anyone lives here now?

Do you get wind of any movement, hear anything?
Your nose, does it get a whiff of something happening?
Or has it all happened – already? Is it over?
Do you think this is meltdown?
Tell me, are any of your senses engaged?
I mean, could you come to court, hand on heart,
and testify that you saw something or someone *stirring*?
I am not, dear friend, asking for anything
as vulgar as agitation in this scene,
still less a rousing song-and-dance routine
choreographed on the stone stairway.

What about a ripple, a flutter, a quiver, a rustle,
a twitch, a rumour of life?

The Venetian maroon drapery on the balustrade:
who threw it down there or who arranged it so?
Did the wife of Pontius Pilate
wearily set down her travelling cloak there
when she landed back, dismissed into exile
when her husband was discharged for cruelty?
Did she never want to see royal red again?
Or is that a luscious bath towel, thrown casually down
by the new model for Chanel on her first shoot?

Never mind the decade,
what century are we in?

No, there is nothing casual or random in this scene:
everything is tonsured, defined, shaped,
engineered, draped, to a forensic precision.
So controlled, I fear a sneeze might cause chaos.

Is this a serial killer's artifice and the detective's nightmare?
Has the killer already dispatched the family offstage?
Was he a student of classical Greek drama,
a follower of the tradition which insisted
that violence should always happen "off-scene"
– "obscene" –
so the worst terror happens offstage, out of view?
Perhaps the real obscenity here is not given to us.
Did the serial killer take that towel, with gloved hands,
from a plastic bag and place it there as disinformation
to distract a division of forensic specialists?

Yesterday evening, after dinner, I pulled my son away
from pulverising exotic thugs on PlayStation
and asked him to look at this painting.
"Daniel," I said, "I need your help.
Tell me, son, what do you think of this?"
The painting lay, by itself, solo, on my desk.

He looked down, then lifted it up, held it in his hands,
absorbed the scene. For all the energy he expends
on his double passion: dinosaurs and computer games –
he has the house and garden littered with beasts
from Allosaurus to Ultrasaurus –
yet he can somehow call himself
to an instant stillness that always astounds.

After two or three wordless minutes,
he put the painting down
and looked up at me, appearing slightly dazed,
as if he'd just emerged from forty days in the desert:
"Dad," he said, "this is seriously evil.
Sorry, I gotta go. Homework for tomorrow. Good night."
And he sprinted up the stairs without another word.
I know "wicked" means good in his dictionary,
but "seriously evil"? I presume it means what it says.

This morning, just before she left for work,
I showed *Villa on the Sea* to Marie-Louise, my wife.
"Is this another of your paintings, Luke?" she asked.
"A quick look. Oh dear, not another still life!
Hmmmm. Strange. Too much composure, darling,
not enough sparkle – a bit like you, I have to say.
Do they have a washing machine inside?
Where is the road out of here?
Is this your idea of a holiday villa,
far from the madding crowd,
away from here and us and dinosaurs?
Anyway, have a good day, darling.
Got to dash. Speak later. Bye."

(My wife talks to me like text messages
thumbed blindly on the run.)

You know how sometimes people catch you
unawares by a throwaway remark;
they're not privy to the impact *that* remark has made on you
as they toss an opinion over their shoulders,
their eyes fixed on exit, keys jangling,
hurrying off to keep an appointment elsewhere.
They leave you behind them, feeling punctured
as you stand behind the door they've closed behind them.

You stupidly wonder if you should run after them
for further explanation. Of course, by then,
they've already driven away, your front door
disappearing in their rear-view mirror,
but not that they have noticed.
Life has already moved on, in pitiless haste,
because life has always somewhere else to go –
away from that stray bullet, away from that mud-slide
that gobbles down everyone and everything in its path –
leaving you alone, like a still life, holding that remark
as if it were a prize gem unexpectedly bequeathed you.

Sometimes I remind myself
of Virginia Woolf's description of Robinson Crusoe:
"a man staring at a pot".

I painted *Villa on the Sea* a month ago.
When I finish any piece I have the strange habit
of covering it with a sheet, turning to fresh work,
and then, after a couple of weeks or so,
returning to the finished painting to take another look.
I question the painting like a stranger
happening on it in a gallery, with a friend;
sometimes I talk to the painting,
but mostly I interrogate my imaginary friend –
you might have guessed my curious habit, dear friend,
when I started this piece.

Only when I talk to the painting
or hear myself question my companion
do I realise what, in my painting, might appear
askew or stilted, what might seem intrusive, irrelevant;
if light and shadow are on speaking terms.
What was it the poet W.H. Auden once wrote?

How do you know what you think
until you see what you say?

I know what I think when I see what I paint.
When I painted *Villa on the Sea*
I did not leave people out;
there were no people to put in.
I have no interest in painting portraits or people;
instead, I try to catch enduring isolation and solitude,
which is why I lean to still life – objects on a table:
a doll's head,
a blue vase,
a pewter candlestick,
which are placed side by side on a surface
but clearly share no sense of togetherness,
not even in the painting, if you understand me.

They just happen to be placed in stylised proximity
for the time it takes to paint them so,
which some people might see as destination.
Why would anyone, with half a brain,
think that proximity means intimacy,
or that distance means division?
By the time you see my still life in a gallery, dear friend,
each piece has already returned to its discrete solitude
with neither memory nor hope of togetherness.

Sometimes I paint an empty road
with a serene unpeopled vista as background,

wondering if viewers will be engaged
by the empty road or the lush landscape, and why.
Or I paint an empty boardwalk fronting an empty beach,
with two warning flags flying –
but rarely is there movement such as this.
One critic called the two flags an aberration…

My wife – a columnist of a well-known daily newspaper –
advises me to paint frenzied storms, like Turner,
or marketplace explosions in Afghanistan or Iraq
a moment after the suicide bomber
has flicked the switch or pulled the cord.
"Fasten on the horror of *that* moment," she instructs me.
"Engage your viewers in extremity; blast them
out of their designer trousers with shock and awe."
I remember she thumped the table to underline her point,
sending the doll's head on its own unscheduled roll.

What can I say to a woman whose profession
is to document the obvious for her readers,
take a stout-hearted stand, in hindsight,
about mistakes and blunders committed in the dark?
With fresh information, any dunderhead can improve history.
She never goes anywhere to see anything for herself –
"I am not a reporter," she keeps saying –
but shares her critical commentary with the waiting world.

And what can I tell her about her painting projects for me?
That, apart from psychopaths, few of her readers
would want to decorate their homes with genocide,
pay to hang carnage on their kitchen wall,
display annihilation above the headboard of their double bed.
Who wants to sleep under human wreckage?
She has no idea of the difference between a word become wise
and a painting struggling for perspective.

There is no hindsight in my paintings,
only premonitions, openings into the dark,
stillness harvested and packed tight in a frame.
I don't chronicle turbulence after arrival –
I am no journalist – I paint turbulence biding its time
like a crouching lion with all the time in the world.

Conflict and disorder are not contained by composure;
anger is nursed and nourished under a thin layer of paint.
Turbulence sleeps beneath every stillness,
keeping to its own unpublished schedule;
then it wakes, without prompting, without warning,
to seize its ravishing time in the sun. There is no denying it.

Perhaps that's why my son, my beloved son,
called *Villa on the Sea* "seriously evil",
because he understood this static world only as interval,
a moment caught in time before volcanic interruption.
Or perhaps he caught something else in his own stillness:
that this is no interval; rather, this is eternal now,
an elegant interment, after the explosion has settled.
Perhaps he thinks the desecration has already happened,
and there is no prospect of new arrivals.

Why can't my wife see in a lifetime
what our beloved son gleans in a moment?
Why does she delude her readers into thinking
that her delayed insights pass for pioneering thinking?
Why can't she see what is under
her nose,
my nose,
our son's nose:
the still life of three proximate people
passing themselves off as a carefree family?

Forgive me, dear friend, if I sound harsh to you.
I am not a hard man, but grateful for more than you know.
Sure, I am a painter of repute, catalogued around the world,
but I am located at a particular address,
married to a particular woman,
sharing a particular son.
Three of us share the same postcode.
I am defined by scrupulous detail.

This painting is my nightmare.
What was it Emily Dickinson wrote?

> *A great Hope fell*
> *You heard no noise*
> *The Ruin was within*
> *Oh cunning wreck that told no tale*
> *And let no Witness in.*

Dear Emily knew well that our kingdoms can fall
soundlessly, leaving not an echo or a discernible trace,
nothing for a future archaeologist to catalogue.
Everything on the taut surface remains
as it has always appeared to be.
Perhaps it takes a while for us to come to see
that our kingdom might have already passed away.
We stubbornly look for prospect,
but what if we behold only history?

As I said to you before about *Villa on the Sea*:
it's so controlled, I fear a sneeze might cause chaos.
What is waiting to happen
sleeps there in the mouldering silence.
What do you think, dear friend, when you look?
Wherever there is water something is sinking;
the sea will take back everything, especially the lion.

You see the winged lion
whose head has failed to keep up
and who has lost heart;
you see a woman's discarded wrap,
her swaddling cover now gone;
you might notice (certainly I do)
the absence of any toys –
not a single discarded dinosaur.
You see the coming of twilight.

The gathered stillness, like kindling, waits for ignition.
Please pray, dear friend,
that no one flicks the switch or pulls the cord.
Please pray that no one even thinks of sneezing.

Peasant Woman with Buckets and a Child

Kasimir Malevich

Bearing up

For Lenore Greene

He took our photograph as we were passing
and then asked if it was all right – Malevich,
he said his name was. I suppose we don't look
like the kind of people you ever need permission from,
do we? I mean, who would be rushing to our door
to crave our seal of approval for anything?
Do we look like we could endorse fresh air?
I've never been asked for my consent for anything,
not even my marriage; so what's a photograph?

He explained he was painting the landscape behind us
from an aerial perspective, a God's-eye view,
and went on and on about surveying from above,
trying to remap the world as a patchwork quilt.
Everything, he said, is a matter of perception:
what you see depends on the angle you choose
as *your* slant on the world, the lookout point
you settle on to decode what you behold.

Then he threw in a by-the-way that he was
Russian Catholic of Polish parents:
was this his slant, I wondered, his lookout point?
I thought, this poor soul is going to take some time,
so I unburdened myself of my yoke,
landed the two buckets of water at his feet
so I could rest the burning crick in my neck
and he could survey the buckets
from an aerial perspective…

I have a compulsion to help, dear onlooker.
What can I tell you? It's in my bent Catholic bones.

The artist paused and looked down into my buckets
like some blindfolded Narcissus
flummoxed at a sudden loss of self,
making out only circles of white and squares of black
that reflected nothing
but what you bring to how you see.
He looked up at me and my daughter,
then back down to the buckets,
as if our two reflections should somehow be captive there.
I wonder if he felt cheated that our peasant water,
opaque with turbulence, blinded himself to himself.

His tone of voice then changed to confessional hush
and he admitted he was getting nowhere
with his painting. Getting nowhere?
Now, I thought, he's talking our language;
straining for horizon, freefalling to nowhere,
this we understood; here is where we live; this is home.
"Nothing," he exclaimed, "is leaping from my palette!"
(When I sneaked a quick peak at his canvas,
I thought: there's nothing leaping
from your painting either.)
He said this as if the two of us grounded souls
would concelebrate in his ritual of lament,
concede that our stone-age frugal sanctuary –
even from God's zenithal point of view –
was only midden, quagmire, bog.

"That's why," he explained, "I took the photograph."
He went on to say he might consider
fronting his landscape with the two of us:
I was dying to ask if we'd be reduced to patchwork

in his painting, but kept my peasant tongue under guard.
He promised that if he did use us, he'd surely send a photo
of his painting to decorate our family album.
Like we surely had one.

How I love the dafties who think that people like us
have volumes of thrilling photographs
to make our neighbours fidget with envy!
As if me and my husband and daughter
have ventured beyond the local marketplace –
we have never been to Kiev, three hours away –
as if we've ready access to airports international
and have lazed beside green swimming pools,
sipped margaritas, dawdled around antique arcades.

Part of being poor is being stuck where you are,
embedded in the landscape like basalt rock,
knowing you'll never need to consult a map.
To get away from this outpost,
we'd need a plane to take us to the nearest bus route!
In our midget village everyone is poor:
there's nothing but other people's poverty
to compare your own with; the struggle to survive
makes everything else seem trivial, unworthy.

Hardship is our daily concelebration,
and we all take turns to preside.
Don't misunderstand me: I am not complaining.
There is no more worthy liturgy to God on high
than the gathered poor breaking the clouds.

You will have noticed, I'm sure, dear onlooker,
wherever you be in the world,
that needy and desperate people make the best laughter.
Only last week the teacher asked my daughter,

"If you have three roubles in your left-hand pocket
and two roubles in your right-hand pocket,
what do you have?"
My daughter replied: "I have someone else's coat on."
How we all laughed at that (including the poor teacher)!

Photographs are for those who travel to exotic places
and meet perpendicular people not stooped by drudgery:
these people lay down diverting memories worth hoarding,
prized moments on which to lean a dull evening.
Back home, ages hence, with time to kill,
they can leaf through a gallery
of antique monuments fronted by themselves –
columns and cenotaphs, palaces and parliaments –
and you know, on looking at the photos,
that the borrowed architecture, that solemn background,
is suddenly trivial beside this grinning individual.
This photo is more valuable than a stamped passport,
for this is visual proof of being somewhere else, away,
away from the slow drip of unchanging days.

Look at the pair of us, dear onlooker:
do we look as if we've travelled even in our dreams?

We only have one picture in our house,
an icon of the Sacred Heart of Jesus.
My beloved husband, my life and my lantern,
lights a candle every night before the picture,
and the three of us kneel and pray to this wounded man,
no stranger to heartache or distress.
We pray to him who looks like one of us,
that we might manage through tomorrow:
our prayer is humble, only for the morrow,
because we are people who've been shaped
to nurse but humble hopes.

So we smiled our consent to Mr Malevich,
the famous artist from Kiev,
and when we explained we didn't have an address –
our house has no number, our street no name –
he kindly noted our names and nearest post office,
dispatching us with promise as we trudged for home.

Of course, we thought we'd never hear again
from Mr Malevich, and when we told my husband
that evening, at supper, of our chancing on the artist,
he laughed and said: "I love you both,
but who would make an icon of the two of you?"
I said, "Dear Karl, you might not recognise us:
we could be broken down as landscape, sea, sky."
"Oh, *Mat'* (Mother)," he said, "in that case
your face will be the moon, your eyes the stars,
and your shoulders, for sure, will be ski slopes,
while little Raisa here will be a sturdy oak tree!"
We laughed and discussed which bits of us
could be turned over into landscape –
the daft things we talk about!

Two months later we were told to collect
a starched envelope from the post office,
and when we opened it – there we were,
my daughter Raisa and me, staring back at ourselves!
How pleased we were that we had made it beyond
the village at last, even if only on paper!

Sure, it's not the photograph Mr Malevich took,
but a photograph of what he made of us;
and how well he caught us in a trembling moment!
I love Mr Malevich for his perspective on us,
truer than any photograph could ever conjure us.
Isn't the man a spiritual mastermind?

Anthropologists – those experts hungry for conformity
who spend their life cataloguing the herd into groupings –
define our tribe by the shape of our shoulders.
The burden and strain of bearing up,
settling for the hand fate has dealt us,
just managing through the day,
scraping for a living, carrying our daily cross:
all this has pressed down on our shoulders.

My stalwart daughter, Raisa,
is already made the same as I've become:
she is no child but a miniature adult,
shaped by evolution for the future that awaits her.
She looks like a cut-out figure from a child's comic,
pressed flat between the pages of a scrapbook.

You must notice our shoulders above all –
Mr Malevich certainly has –
how they've been worn down, over time,
from being square-shaped to egg-shaped.
We have shifted, peddled, hawked, carried,
lugged, humped, sustained so much over the years
that soon our peasant shoulders will have no grip
to bear even the weightless Christ-child,
should he happen by, looking to cross our stream.
Saint Christopher did not belong to our tribe, for sure.

My husband was right, after all:
our shoulders might as well be ski slopes;
steep inclines for whatever lands to slither down.
Soon our sunken spines will press for early retirement
and the right to fold themselves away.
After another generation, what will we hold?

Oh, we have put our shoulder to the wheel,
we have buckled down and buckled under
until all we are is the legion of the buckled.
You notice I have to use my neck muscles
to carry the yoke that holds the buckets.
My husband Karl calls me, "My beautiful ox,
my beast of burden, my carry-all!"

He is the kindest man in all the Russias
and works as the village blacksmith –
all hammer and tongs, he is.
He forges farming tools and metalwork for wagons,
like the iron bands for cartwheels.
The fire is lit with charcoal from pine and beech wood,
and the water I carry is for his hollowed-out beam
which he uses as a quenching trough
where fired horseshoes are cooled in water.
Most of his time is spent, back bent,
hammering on the anvil, sparking the dark,
to shape wrought-iron shoes for beasts of burden.

I tell him we should be shod like them.

Look at us: we are all frontal view;
our bent necks have disappeared from view
behind our flattened faces: we are one-dimensional
in the tradition of our Russian icons.
In our icons we believe reality cannot be captured:
there is no mimicking of the physical world;
there are no shadows in our icons
because they're a depiction of the mystical.

Behind us is a sprawling map,
where neither rise nor fall is heeded;

everything is on the level, flush, plumb, plane.
Is this how the hawk eyes us from the heights,
a world spreadeagled for his keen appraisal?
The punctured hills, the levelled shore, the glassy sea?
The two boats, hauled onto the shore,
have been flattened into black surfboards.
Raisa thought they looked like giant footprints
left behind by Atlas.

Malevich has caught our spirit well,
in bondage to our flesh and bones.
Look, dear onlooker, at our broad backs;
continue down along our thickset trunk and legs
to the spread of our bare feet and sprawling toes.
How I love the artist's flat view of our feet,
as if they were grafted onto Mother Earth
and needed levering off for fulsome viewing!
Our legs are cedars of Lebanon
anchored in Ukraine.

We have hands to dig like navvies,
each iron digit forged to rupture rocks
and subjugate the earth.
We were created to till the soil,
to turn the earth, to bend, to dig, to plough,
to plant, to scatter, to wait, to gather, to carry.
Infinity of active verbs we are, and there is no subtlety
in our body language, no conditional tense.

Our hands and legs and shoulders define us:
our faces are added extras, as you can see,
like painted Easter eggs,
tacked on, an afterthought,
when the main framework has been shaped.
I do like the way Malevich kept the makings

of a wry puzzled smile on my face, I must say,
although I see my bumper breasts,
my proud cupolas, have been razed to the ground.

The priest told us last Sunday at Mass
that we are *Corpus Christi* – the body of Christ.
He asked us to think of what happened to Jesus' body,
the body that was catapulted into the passive voice:
the body that was taken, led away, handed over, abused,
stripped, nailed, reviled, and crucified to death.

He quoted the lines of a hymn that is my favourite:

> *Come see his hands and his feet,*
> *the scars that speak of sacrifice,*
> *hands that flung stars into space,*
> *to cruel nails surrendered.*

He asked us to think of the eyes, the bruised eyes,
hooded not by Olympian laurel but by spiky thorns,
that looked down from the cross with forgiveness
on those doing novenas to the Angel of Death.
Hear the voice, he said, that bade a crushed people:
"Come to me all you who labour and are overburdened
and I will give you rest. Take my yoke upon you."
Think, our priest said, of the shoulders
that shored up the weight of burdens not his,
that caved in under the leaden muscle of the cross.

"This was *his* body," the priest said,
"the body that could endure no more
and resigned, folded itself into death.
Through his body all our bodies are graced.
Never, never, never, whatever shape you are,

whatever shape you're in, belittle or disparage
the beauty and glory of your own body!
What you were given and who you've become,
this is how you grace a broken world!"

Through body comes grace:
hard to believe, but Malevich helps me to believe.
He calls us peasants *krestjane* – "the baptised ones" –
the little people baptised into the body of Christ,
the ones destined to take up their cross and follow the Lord,
to walk the Via Dolorosa
that winds its ways through our streets and villages.
We are the bowed and the bent ones,
the bodies appointed to share his suffering
and carry the cross on behalf of a fractured world.

Malevich even included in his painting
the animal that dominates the Passion story,
the cock that crowed at the high priest's palace
and, three times, arrested poor Saint Peter
after he had denied his Master and Lord.
You will have noticed the cock, dear onlooker,
head down, in the painting, at Raisa's right arm.

When Peter, leading witness, denied himself and Jesus
to the little girl, the doorkeeper who monitored
all surveillance, all entrances and exits to the palace,
it must have sounded to Peter's ears
as if every animal in the world was baying
and howling at such forsaking of their Maker.
Sometimes our world is sound, not space.

But this cock is not dominant in our story,
does not throat his triple accusations
or caw alarm, but pecks, almost invisibly,

at that thin field of yellow corn.
Thank you, Mr Malevich, for this,
for painting us for who we really are,
with the cock, head down, at ease, beside us.

We shoulder our cross on behalf of
a world in bits, fractured, levelled, prostrate –
the world that Malevich sees so clearly.
It is this belief that enables me and Karl and Raisa
to trudge on, keep going,
even sometimes to work up a smile
at those who look on, wondering why.

Look at us, dear onlooker,
and behold *Corpus Christi*...

Pietà

Vincent Van Gogh

Letting go

For the priests and people of St Mary's, Navan, Ireland

Behold my son,
my beloved son, Jesus!
Would that I had died
instead of you!

Sorry, Son,
I've let you go just for a moment,
released my hold on you,
as I appeal to whoever is looking at us,
whoever is out there,
the onlookers.
I need to protest about what has happened to you,
you poor soul.
Please don't fall on me now
and hurt yourself on the hard rock.

I need to do this
because there were no protests at your crucifixion, Son,
no organised marches, no interest groups,
no angry followers making their presence felt.
Where were all the people you healed,
the poor wretched souls you saved from torment?
Where were the hungry people you'd fed in the hills?

Why were so few of us there?

There was nobody there carrying a placard,
protesting, "This man is innocent!"
"Free the prisoner!"

Where were all the men who tramped behind you
along the roads and through the villages of Galilee?
Where are they now?
When you were stumbling along the Via Dolorosa
and you looked over your shoulder
to see who was following you,
who did you see?

Why is it that it's the women
who turn up in the hard places,
to watch, to attend, to wait?
Why is it that we are the ones who're always left
to pick up the pieces
when the men have had their brutal sport?

Beneath your buckled body on the cross,
there was only still life:
bowed heads,
hooded eyes,
the averted gaze;
deluded soldiers standing stiff,
chief priests impatient for your death,
two demented thieves on either side of you,
one lonely disciple,
and three Marys, hands clasped,
standing together but utterly alone.

And over everything there was silence,
silence black as night
and deep as God.

The silence was shattered
by your scream of abandonment
when you left us,

and we made your prayer our own:
"My God, my God, why have you abandoned us?"

Sorry, Son,
I'm back,
back holding you again,
surrounding you with my arms,
flesh of my flesh.

Look at you now,
blistered, limp, lifeless,
terminated, altogether dead.
Ecce homo indeed…

You know, I always imagined
the reverse of this scene,
that you would attend me on my deathbed,
that you would appear –
soft as an evening breeze –
alone, just by yourself,
without your sad friends,
and sit with me
and gather me in your arms
and speak the gentle words
you always spoke to strangers,
but this time you would speak them to me,
flesh of your flesh,
until I finally went from your embrace
to the embrace of your God and my God.

Look at us now…

No mother expects to outlive her child;
no mother expects to hold

the body of her dead child in her arms;
for she can tender no comfort,
whisper no lullabies,
offer no healing kiss that might be felt
to make a difference.

What can I do?
What can I say
that will make any difference?

Remember when you were a child,
a lively little upstart, you were,
and you would rush into the house
after you'd fallen over a rock or something
and you would cry out, "Oh, Mammy, look!"
And you would solemnly point
to your bruised knee or elbow,
and I would drop whatever I was doing
and anxiously run to attend you
and wash your cut or scratch,
all the time hiding my laughter.
And then I'd rub oil on your little hurt
and kiss it better?

Remember?

You won't remember, Son,
but I remember well
when I carried you as a newborn child –
a four-day walk, it was –
up to the Temple in Jerusalem,
to present you to the Lord,
according to our custom.

You cried for most of the way,
and your father – God bless his kind heart –
wanted to take you home to Nazareth
to see a doctor.
I remember he joked, saying,
maybe you weren't shaped for going south,
maybe you were a real northerner, a highlander,
so that the farther south you went
the more your health would decline!

How the two of us laughed;
you cried.
The three of us got there eventually.

I remember when we arrived in the Temple,
I handed you over
to the old prophet, Simeon,
who held you in his arms
shivering with excitement.
I watched this ancient holy man,
as wrinkled as an old olive tree,
hold you, newly born, in his arms,
like he was holding the breath of God.

He spoke words about you
that I did not understand then
and don't understand now.
He prayed:

> *Now, Lord,*
> *you can let your servant go in peace*
> *according to your word;*
> *for my eyes have seen the salvation*
> *which you have prepared*
> *before the face of all people –*

a light to enlighten the Gentiles,
and the glory of your people Israel.

I remember his words well,
but tell me this, Son:
how is your broken body,
this corpse I hold in my arms,
a light to anyone,
the glory of anything?
Tell me, Son,
where is the light?
And where, oh where, is the glory?

I never told you this before,
but old Simeon
cautioned me that day in the Temple
that my heart would be broken in two
because of you.
"This child is destined for the fall and the rising
of many in Israel," he declared.
Then he leaned over to me and whispered,
"A sword shall pierce your soul."

Imagine any mother hearing that?
Every mother's nightmare, isn't it,
that her child will wound her sorely,
a dagger thrust through her very soul?

I kept that to myself all these years –
never told a living soul –
because I had no mind to worry you or hurt you.
Certainly, that bit of old Simeon's prophecy
has come true, hasn't it?
From the beginning, you see, I knew
we'd never be a normal happy family.

Sorry, Son, just let me shift your weight a little,
ease you onto my right knee – the good one –
for it's a long while since I cradled you like this.

There, that's better, thanks.

You know the others are waiting inside the tomb
for me to let go of you
and give you up
so they can lay your body
out on the slab
and we can close this borrowed tomb
and go back to whatever is left of life.

But I want to hold you a little longer,
flesh of my flesh:
you are the best part of me.
Before you came along I was nothing,
I was nobody.
You made me, you know.
So let me hug the coldness of you a little longer,
even though I know I have to let you go.

Last times are very precious
and we never did have a last time together,
just the two of us.
I mean time alone, Son,
just us,
being together again,
having our silly little laughs like we used to,
with you teasing me,
like you always did, remember?
Remember how you always made fun of me,
about how long it took me to dress up
before going to the synagogue on the Sabbath.

And you would laugh and say,
"Oh, Mammy, you're only going up the street!"

You were always so casual,
so relaxed about religion,
like you could go before God
wearing anything or nothing!
And here you are now
naked under this old wrap
I made for you ages ago
to keep out the cold.

There are so many questions
I want to ask you, Son, before you go,
so many questions.

Why did you do what you did?
What drove you
to leave the safety of our home in Nazareth
and head out the road, away from us,
putting yourself in harm's way?

Why did you take on the important people
and lacerate them in the public squares?
Why did you tell the chief priests
that the prostitutes would walk before them
into the kingdom of God?

Can you imagine how I felt
when I heard about this from the neighbours?

More than anything else, every mother wants
safety and security for her child
and that is all I ever wanted for you.

I prayed so hard that you would retire
from this dangerous mission of yours,
get a regular job, maybe get big Simon Peter
to teach you how to fish,
so you could settle down in a wee cottage
by the Lake of Galilee.
And rest yourself.

Never told you that before, either.

How could you so quickly forget, Son,
what happened to your teacher, John the Baptist,
who was executed for speaking out
against the authorities?
Weren't you at all anxious
that you might suffer the same fate?
Why did you stubbornly head for
the city of Jerusalem, the prophets' graveyard?
We are simple country folk, Son,
not at ease in the big city.
Didn't you know that this city
is a troublemaker's paradise,
and that the authorities here
calculate every breath you take?
Why did you ignore
the advice of your own disciples
and come here
as if you had an appointment with death?

Why?

Oh, I'm not angry with you, Son,
believe me,
just disappointed that it all had to end

in this brutal way.
And I feel hopelessly sad that we didn't have
more time together.

Time, time, time:
there's always plenty of it
when you don't need it
and little of it when you do.
Now, it's upon us again:
the shadows are lengthening
and the sun is beginning to set
in the world behind me;
it has already set in your world, Son,
and also in mine,
and I doubt it will ever rise again.

I see the others coming now
to take you from me
and lay you down.
Passover is upon us:
we have to go.

You leave life as you came into it,
in your mother's arms,
and now I have to let you go
for the last time.

Goodbye, Son,
I love you,
always have,
always will,
for ever
more.

The Reconciliation of Peter

Iain McKillop

When words are not enough

For Ellen McBride

I roared out the word "Never!" in the graveyard
of the Kidron Valley where the Master,
heading for Gethsemane,
stopped us in our tracks by saying:
"You will all be scandalised by me and run away."
Who was he talking about?
Not me, for sure, I thought! The others?
I countered by admitting that the other ten disciples
(Judas had already passed through traitor's gate)
might well lose faith in him and cut and run,
but persisted that I, Peter, would be a sure exception;
I'd be his stubborn follower to the ends of the earth.

The Master looked aggrieved –
I saw his face in the light of the full moon –
and he said, "This very night, Peter, you will disown me,
not once but three times. You will, believe me, you will."
"Never!" I protested,
loud enough to wake the dead,
and thankfully my other friends supported me in chorus.
But the Master absorbed the echo of our returning voices
and then shrugged his shoulders as if to say,
"We'll see whose estimate comes true."
He said nothing, of course,
but led us in silence to the garden.
That night, two prophecies collided in a graveyard:
one of them, for sure, would join the dead all around.

Sometimes words are not enough.
Sometimes a spoken word is snatched away

briskly by the wind and is dispatched, first north,
whirling through the streets and villages of Lower Galilee,
gaining ground on inclines and on hills,
then is turned around, without notice,
switching direction,
shifting east-south-east across to the Lake of Galilee,
then due south through Samaria and the Jordan Valley,
gradually losing force the more southwards it proceeds,
struggling to rise above the Mount of Olives,
turning south-east, until finally,
when the wind loses any zest it might have had,
the word peters out and is dismissed into the Dead Sea.

The brief biography of a word I said: "Never."

Sometimes words are not enough
because they have no stamina for journey's end.
I didn't know then what I know now,
that "never" is the longest word in any language
no matter how insistently declared.
There are other words, kind words,
whispered in forgiveness,
that are instantly distrusted: too good to be true, you think.
Sometimes you can't believe your ears – so you don't.
Or sometimes your ears are so numbed by spoken words
that you yearn for a gesture not a speech,
a touch rather than another long-winded sermon.
Deaf people, after all, need signs, hand-signals,
and, if blind as well, tracery on the skin.

Sometimes, dear friend, you need to feel forgiveness
in your bones because you're no longer convinced
in your mind
that you can hold out for mercy
on account of the wretched things you've done.
While we all deserve justice, none of us deserves mercy:

we have no birthright to mercy;
no warrant for reprieve,
no entitlement to walk away
after we've shattered someone's life.

We can only hunger for the day when those who hold
our sin in custody, incarcerated in their heart,
will let the hostage go and free us for a future.
That is why the weight of our betrayals
can obliterate whatever faith
we had in absolution,
whatever hope we might have cherished
in being pardoned.
Sometimes darkness invades your soul
and becomes landlord of your life.

The Master knew this in the wisdom of his heart;
he sensed this, and, sensing it,
acted out the drama of his senses.
He understood that sometimes
Gospel is inadequate as word
but must impress itself as touch, as spittle, as breath,
as caress, even as unscheduled tears
that take you by surprise.
Maybe that is why he left us his body, not his mind:
"Take, eat, this is my body given for you."

I remember, because I used to follow him,
watching how he reached out to wearied people
through his body.
Those eyes that hungered beyond the edges of a crowd
for those whom life had disinherited and spurned –
oh, he could spot them a mile away –
and beguile them from their hideouts into welcome.
The voice that sponsored the poor and censured the rich,
confronted the harshness of religious authority –

whose pomposity he openly derided –
whose charism was to overburden little people
and wear them down,
then keep their hands fastened to their side.

And those ears of his that could hear dough rise to bread,
ears ever alert to the shiftiness of life,
the emotional weight of stories,
that never shunned the howling of the broken-hearted,
the ones buckled and distorted, just like me.
The hands that cradled people without crushing them,
then lifted them up, cupped them
like a golden chalice offered to God.
The nose that breathed in
the fragrance of the lilies of the field
and never looked down on any living soul.
The feet that trudged through the underneath of life,
bringing relief to the wavering flames and the bruised reeds,
and would, in time, stagger up a hill called Golgotha
to be tacked down to lumber.

This was his body,
and through his body
came the grace of our Lord Jesus Christ.
Through his body now, dear friend, I am made to feel
not the grip of arrest for what I've done
but the clench of forgiveness because of who *he* is,
his wrestling clasp of love that gathers me in his arms
and wordlessly, yes wordlessly,
insists itself into my flesh.

Sometimes words are not enough.

Have you ever been embraced by a ghost?
While I knew the Master was vulnerable in life,
I thought he was unkillable,
but events have proved me wrong.
I never thought, however, that he could outstrip the tomb,
but events have proved me wrong again.
What do I know?
Don't look to me for insight, dear friend.
But he always taught us
that there was something worse than being put to death:
that was learning to be dead in the midst of life.
Being dead, he argued, was something people
can learn to live with,
so they decorate their tomb and call it home.

I remember the Master once telling a parable
of a father who had two sons and who lost them both:
one was lost in a faraway place
and the other was lost at home.
I remember interrupting Jesus (I did in those days)
asking him how anyone could get lost in his own house.
He insisted you don't need to *go* anywhere to be lost:
you can get lost in the middle of your own family,
you can get lost in the middle of your own community,
even in the middle of your own stillness, he said.

He asked me if he could continue the story,
and I nodded, stupidly.
The family, he explained, broke up when the younger son
sold his portion of the land and scampered off abroad
to sample the delights of a waiting world.
But when he ran out of money and into a famine,
the dream of freedom vanished
and hunger lorded it over the land:
suddenly the young Jewish boy was

no longer a moneyed traveller
but a destitute foreigner far from home.

Suddenly he was just another refugee,
another migrant worker,
another drifter scouring the neighbourhood
for an unlocked door.
His mind confused,
his stomach made a decision to go home,
and on his way back the son rehearsed a speech
that might persuade his father
to accept him back as servant –
if only he could find the proper words.

But the great news is that the father
isn't bothered about speeches,
either hearing them or making them,
when he runs to greet his son.
He doesn't say anything to his come-back son,
not a single word!
He knows that sometimes words are not enough.

Instead the old man pulls his son into his antique body
and weeps down the nape of his neck,
clasping his lost son in sheer utter itching delight,
hoping he can raise the living dead by grip of love.
The old man's language is in his body,
in the silent aching reassurance of welcome home.

The elder brother in the story
stays outside the house,
bawling word after word after word at his father –
he thinks that words can mend his shattered world.
Word upon word rises up
like a wave of ancient sores ungraved
that weep again and flaunt past injuries afresh.

Ever anxious to remind his father of unwavering loyalty
through all the years, and his enduring obedience,
he calculates the arithmetic of fidelity,
reckoning that after the total count,
it amounts to very little in this family.
What reward loyalty?
You might as well be dead.

When Jesus had finished the whole story,
he asked the twelve of us what we thought it meant.

Of course, I popped up immediately and said:
"Master, Master, I think I've got this one!
Don't laugh, no, really, I think I have, honest!
The three people in the story are in each of us.
There is a father inside each of us," I said, "who knows
when to run and enfold the muddled losers in compassion:
he is the one who has a nose for when a party's needed.
There is a younger son in each of us," I said,
"who turns his back on everything he's been given
and heads off to experience everything he shouldn't,
his hopeless judgement leading him repeatedly into danger:
he's the one who'll always need affection and forgiveness.
And then there's an elder brother in each of us," I said,
"who disapproves of everyone who's not like him:
he's the one who wants to make everyone else pay
the price for his loveless fidelity.
All three abide in us," I said, "the only question is:
which of the three of them, which one will shine in us?"

There was silence for a few moments, which worried me,
but then the Master, I remember,
laughed and laughed in delight,
the sound pealing around the hills of Lower Galilee,
resounding like some great gong that could go on for ever.
He clapped me on the back and said,

"Oh, Peter, Peter, even I didn't think of that!
Aren't you great to think of that?"
Then looking at each of us, all twelve,
without missing any of us, he said:
"Believe me, you will do greater things than I have done.
You are the light of the world – so shine!
You are the salt of the earth – so give taste to life!"

Oh, look at me now, dear friend:
some light of the world I am!
When that little porter girl,
younger than my own daughter,
opened the door of the high priest's palace
three nights ago
and lifted the lantern to light up my face,
she shouted out,
"Ah, you're one of *them*, I can see you!"
Bawled it out,
like she had just won a game of hide-and-seek…

I was so scared that I'd be led away and handed over,
then stripped and brutalised by experts in their field
accustomed to crunching bones and slicing skin,
just like they did to the Master –
please understand I have no tolerance for pain –
that I denied my own discipleship,
the heart of who I am and ever want to be.

Twice more the girl and attendants
asked me who I was,
and in renouncing who I was,
I denied belonging to the Master.
Just as the cock crew,
Jesus was led past and looked me in the eye.
It wasn't a look that accused:

"How could you do this to me?"
Nor was it a look that declared:
"Didn't I tell you?"
It was just a sorrowful look
between one sad friend and another,
one that will tether me to that moment
all my days and all my nights.

You might wonder why I turn away,
but how can I ever look him in the face again?

I ran away from the mad city of Jerusalem,
with its talent for debasement and brutality,
ran away from doorkeepers and priests and soldiers,
ran away from accusers and attendants,
ran away from the one I had followed,
leaving him utterly alone to face his certain fate.

I ran, like the others, because we were afraid
the authorities would want to cancel us,
because we were his disciples,
committed to furthering his radical kingdom.
But they are not interested in us,
calculating, given the intelligence they'd gathered,
that we would pose a threat to no one.
Although I was relieved, I admit,
the relief was overshadowed by embarrassment
that we didn't register in their estimate of likely threats.
What is worse, dear friend:
to be hunted down as a real menace to society
or ignored as just another nobody?

And as I ran north,
with the south behind me, forever over my shoulder,
I listened between footfalls

to the voice commanding me away.
This was no Sabbath jaunt, believe me,
this was running for my life.

I ran back home, up here, to the Lake of Galilee,
hoping to erase the memory of his spell as Master,
back to the safety of family, home, seashore, hillside,
back to the rhythm of ordinary time, to return
to something I know I can get right – fishing the lake.
Back to being what I used to be before I met him.

Can you imagine, dear friend, going back home
out of season, to face discreet enquiries
from family and friends:
"You're back already?"
"We didn't expect you back so soon."
"What have you been doing while you were away?"
"Anything exciting happened?"
"You look exhausted! What have you been up to?"
"So, how was life in the big city?"
How could I tell them? What could I say?

Anyway, I'm here now, back here, again.
Here is the place where he first called me,
invited me to follow him, promising me
that he would make something of me.
He nicknamed me in Aramaic, our own language, *Kēphâ*
a clever nickname – "Rocky" – because it means
two different things, like night and day:
it can mean reliable and firm
or it can mean wobbly and shaky.
I know and you know, dear friend, which one I've become.
Oh, I've swung back and forth: believed and doubted,
followed and discarded; loved and disowned.
What has become of me?

Now the Master has returned back here
to interrupt my life again,
to find me again by the lake,
forgive me again, call me again.
But this time he does not call with words
because sometimes words are not enough.
You see me turn my back on him – again –
and this time turn away in shame rather than fear.
As I said to him before,
"Oh, leave me alone, Lord, I am a sinner."
I recognised it then; am sorely aware now.

From where you look,
you cannot see the four fishing boats
returning from another night's catch,
with blue lanterns lit that bob up and down
like falling stars caught in the sails.
They look strangely insubstantial in this setting,
like ghost ships drifting out of their element,
ill at ease in the gathering light.
I should be out there with them, not here with him.
I wish he'd leave me alone,
leave me an exile in my own home
and choose a different crowd to follow him,
pick a more trustworthy leader to count on,
someone who won't embarrass him by cowardice.

I mean, why doesn't he make a fresh start
rather than hold on to the likes of us?
We are a poor investment for a kingdom such as his.

As the darkness is being drained away
I can hear the lake listening;
I can hear the lapping waters whisper soft words,
to leave this shore behind me, head for the horizon,

embrace the deep, and plumb the depths again.
Or am I imagining things?
Beyond my imagination is
what is happening now.

You see the Master, on the edge of the lake,
just as dawn is beginning to break,
pressing forgiveness into my crumpled spirit.
You see me, head downwards, eyes tight shut,
hands by his side,
a shrivelled blind man fingering for hope.
It feels like the Master's shouldering me forwards,
unlocking my feet from the rocks on which I stand
and nudging me into the shallows of the lake.

After all the Master has endured,
his wounds have now become his signature,
and he signs himself in my flesh.
He presses, crunches me so hard that you can see
the tracery of fresh red
as his wounds begin to open again.

Sometimes words are not enough,
so his wounds become his clinching argument.
"By his wounds we are healed."